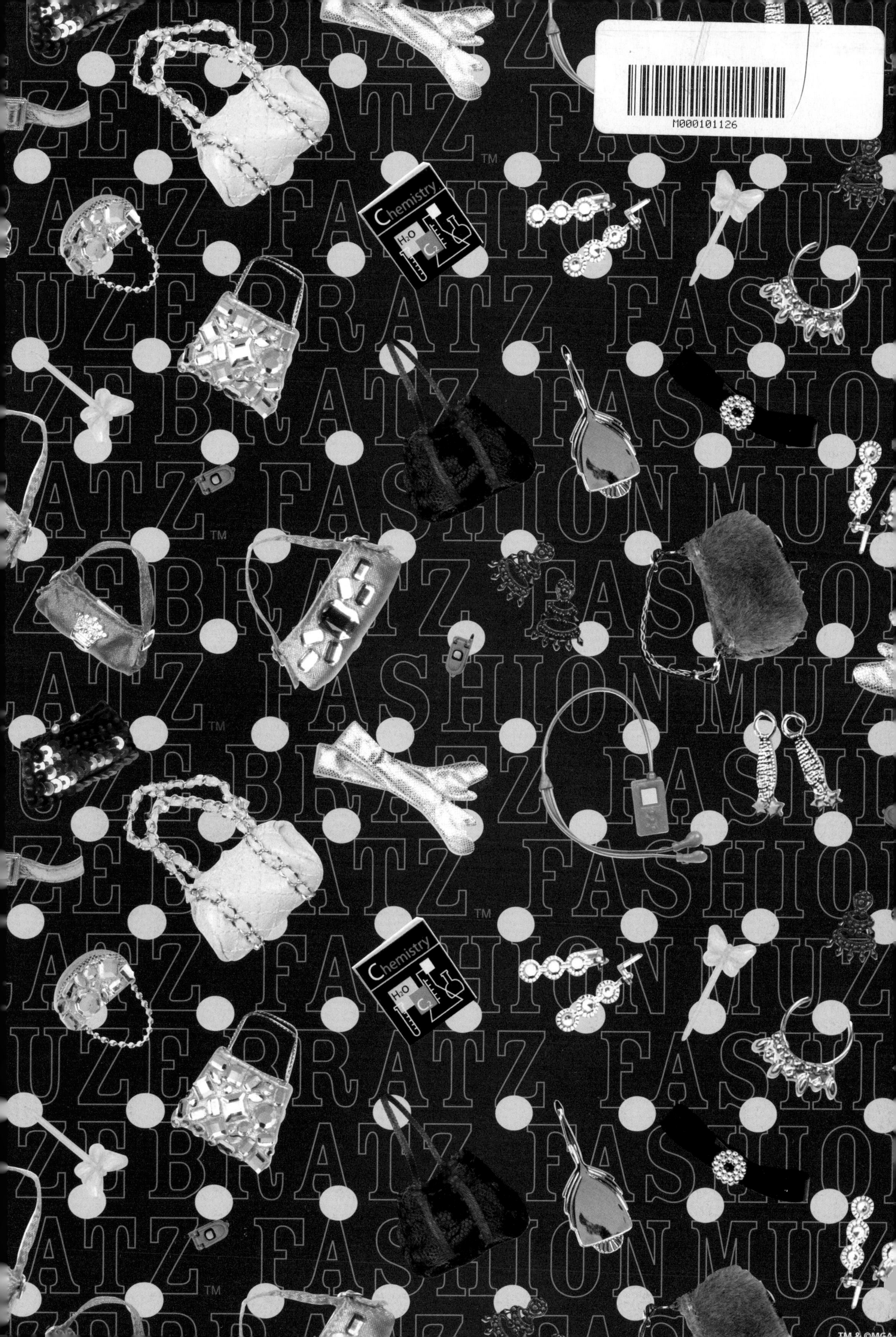
Chemistry

CONTENTS

Published 2008
Published by Pedigree Books LTD, Beech Hill House, Walnut Gardens, Exeter, Devon EX4 4DH books@pedigreegroup.co.uk

BRATZ™

ANNUAL 2009

£7.99

http://www.myprofile.com/yasmin

HOME | ABOUT ME | EXPLORE

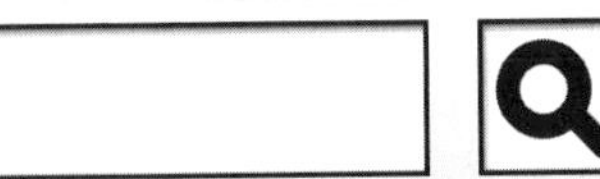

Search

Find more friends

Birthdays

Birthdays this week:

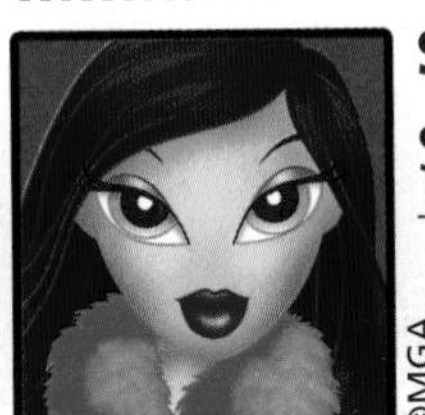

©MGA

Sasha

Send a Card

Groups

Stiles High Girls with a passion for fashion!

Yasmin's Charity Run Fund

Writer's Group

We Went to Stilesville Elementary School

The Movie Club

Animal Lovers

Profile

©MGA

Yasmin™

Today I'm: looking after an adorable tabby kitten.

Hometown: Stilesville

School: Stiles High

Activities: Writing, reading, animal care, charity work.

Interests: Literature, fashion, being with my BFFs.

Favourite music: Coldplay.

Favourite books: Classics, modern literature.

Notice Board

Show All | **Today** | Yesterday | Last Week

Displaying 1–5 of 89 notices.

At 6:05pm yesterday **Sasha** said

See you at Angel's!

At 5:45pm yesterday **Katia** said

Can't believe I'm missing out on Angel's baking! See you on Monday!

At 5:30pm yesterday **Cloe** said

Are you coming over for cupcakes?

At 12:15pm yesterday **Jade** said

Where's the tabby cat from, girl? How do those lil' strays know to come to you?

At 7:45am yesterday **Siernna** said

Hey Pretty Princess, I'm just heading out for a run if you want to come?

FORUM GROUPS CREATE

Friends

Mutual | See All | Groups | Find New

 **Cameron** is thinking about a certain someone . . .

 **Cloe** is lazing in the sun and catching up on some reading . . . my fave celebrity mags!

 **Dana** is enjoying my strawberry smoothie.

 **Dylan** is mainly thinking about food.

 **Felicia** is looking forward to a girls' night out!

 **Fianna** is such a sleepyhead today!

 **Jade** is checking out the new fashion boutique in the mall.

 **Katia** is back in Stilesville on Monday – yay!

 **Kumi** can't wait to get the photos developed!

 **Maribel** is looking forward to the weekend.

 **Meygan** is giving in to temptation – those cupcakes are irresistible!

 **Nevra** is about to go to dance class.

 **Phoebe** is having a bad hair day – help me, girls!

 **Roxxi** is losing my voice – sympathy required!

 **Sasha** is organising my desk.

 **Siernna** is making like Cloe and turning my nails into works of art!

 **Vinessa** is tired of homework!

Music

Photos

1 Album

Good Times

Latest News

Yasmin wrote on **Sasha's** notice board. 6:04pm

Yasmin wrote on **Cloe's** notice board. 6:03pm

Yasmin commented on **Jade's** photo. 5:39pm "This was definitely the hottest look of the day!"

Yasmin tagged **Vinessa** in 9 photos. 12:15pm

Yasmin created the group **Yasmin's** Charity Run Fund. 12:10pm

Yasmin is looking after an adorable tabby kitten. 12:02pm

Search

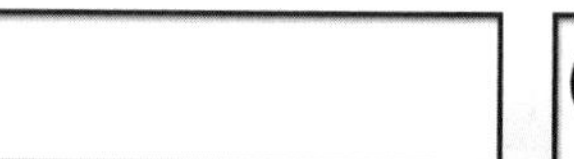

Find more friends

Messages

Fun Stuff

Photos

1 Album

©MGA

BFFs

Groups

Stiles High Girls with a passion for fashion!

Yasmin's Charity Run Fund

Stiles High Art Trip

We Went to Stilesville Elementary School

The Movie Club

Stiles High Tennis Team

Profile

©MGA

Cloe™

Today I'm: lazing in the sun and catching up on some reading . . . my fave celebrity mags!

Hometown: Stilesville

School: Stiles High

Activities: Art, tennis, sunbathing.

Interests: Fashion, art, hanging out with my BFFs.

Favourite music: Fun, funky pop. Anything hot and new!

Favourite books: Exciting mysteries with happy endings!

Notice Board

Show All | **Today** | Yesterday | Last Week

Displaying 1–5 of 103 notices.

At 6:03pm yesterday **Yasmin** said
I'll be there in five!

At 6:01pm yesterday **Dylan** said
*Are the guys invited for cupcakes too, **Angel?***

At 5:57pm yesterday **Jade** said
Count me in.

At 5:54pm yesterday **Sasha** said
I'm just finishing organising my desk – save some for me!

At 5:50pm yesterday **Cameron** said
Sounds great – I'm there! Thanks for the invitation . . .

FORUM GROUPS CREATE

Friends

Mutual | See All | Groups | Find New

 **Cameron** is thinking about a certain someone . . .

 **Dana** is enjoying my strawberry smoothie.

 **Dylan** is mainly thinking about food.

 **Felicia** is looking forward to a girls' night out!

 **Fianna** is such a sleepyhead today!

 **Jade** is checking out the new fashion boutique in the mall.

 **Katia** is back in Stilesville on Monday – yay!

 **Kumi** can't wait to get the photos developed!

 **Maribel** is looking forward to the weekend.

 **Meygan** is giving in to temptation – those cupcakes are irresistible!

 **Nevra** is about to go to dance class.

 **Phoebe** is having a bad hair day – help me, girls!

 **Roxxi** is losing my voice – sympathy required!

 **Sasha** is organising my desk.

 **Siernna** is making like Cloe and turning my nails into works of art!

 **Vinessa** is tired of homework!

 **Yasmin** is looking after an adorable tabby kitten.

Music

Birthdays

Latest News

Cloe wrote on **Dylan's** notice board. 6:03pm

Cloe wrote on **Cameron's** notice board. 5:51pm

Cloe commented on **Jade's** photo. 5:37pm *"Girl, you are so fashion forward it's scary!"*

Cloe wrote on **Yasmin's** notice board. 5:30pm

Cloe is going to make cupcakes – all friends invited to try them at about six tonight! 4:08pm

Cloe tagged herself in 3 photos. 3:48pm

Cloe joined the group **Yasmin's** Charity Run Fund. 12:30pm

Cloe joined the group Stiles High Tennis Team. 11:59am

Cloe wrote on **Jade's** notice board. 11:30am

http://www.myprofile.com/jade

HOME | ABOUT ME | EXPLORE

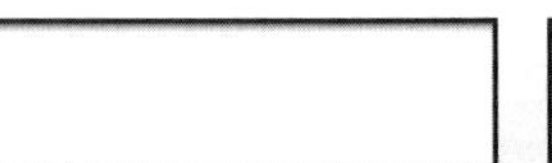

Find more friends

X Birthdays

Birthdays this week:

Sasha

Send a Card

X Groups

Stiles High Girls with a passion for fashion!

Yasmin's Charity Run Fund

Fashion Trend Predictions

We Went to Stilesville Elementary School

The Movie Club

X Profile

Jade™

Today I'm: checking out the new fashion boutique in the mall.

Hometown:	Stilesville
School:	Stiles High
Activities:	Fashion designing, magazine editor.
Interests:	Fashion!
Favourite music:	Gwen Stefani – girls with attitude!
Favourite books:	Non-fiction books about the history of fashion, pop-culture, art and all the major trend-setters.

X Notice Board

Show All | **Today** | Yesterday | Last Week

Displaying 1–5 of 567 notices.

At 11:30am yesterday **Cloe** said
Don't even go there, Bunny Boo!

At 11:23am yesterday **Sasha** said
Of course Cameron WOULD think that

At 11:09am yesterday **Cameron** said
The best outfit was the one Cloe modelled.

At 10:46am yesterday **Sasha** said
I could help you to organise the next one if you like?

At 10:28am yesterday **Dylan** said
Kool Kat, your fashion show ROCKED last night!

FORUM GROUPS CREATE

Friends

Mutual | See All | Groups | Find New

 **Cameron** is thinking about a certain someone . . .

 **Cloe** is lazing in the sun and catching up on some reading . . . my fave celebrity mags!

 **Dana** is enjoying my strawberry smoothie.

 **Dylan** is mainly thinking about food.

 **Felicia** is looking forward to a girls' night out!

 **Fianna** is such a sleepyhead today!

 **Katia** is back in Stilesville on Monday – yay!

 **Kumi** can't wait to get the photos developed!

 **Maribel** is looking forward to the weekend.

 **Meygan** is giving in to temptation – those cupcakes are irresistible!

 **Nevra** is about to go to dance class.

 **Phoebe** is having a bad hair day – help me, girls!

 **Roxxi** is losing my voice – sympathy required!

 **Sasha** is organising my desk.

 **Siernna** is making like Cloe and turning my nails into works of art!

 **Vinessa** is tired of homework!

 **Yasmin** is looking after an adorable tabby kitten.

Music

Photos

2 Albums

©MGA

Fabulous Fashion Show

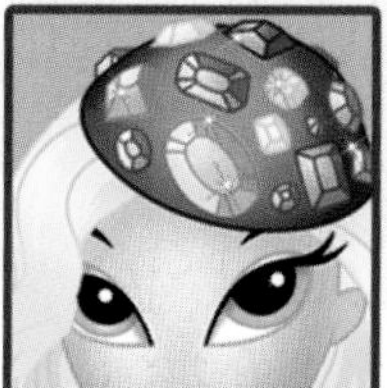

©MGA

My new designs - comments please!

Latest News

Jade wrote on **Cloe's** notice board. 5:57pm

Jade joined the group **Yasmin's** Charity Run Fund. 12:30pm

Jade wrote on **Yasmin's** notice board. 12:15pm

Jade wrote on **Sasha's** notice board. 10:58am

Jade is checking out the new fashion boutique in the mall. 9:30am

Jade tagged herself in 10 photos. 9:26am

http://www.myprofile.com/sasha

HOME | ABOUT ME | EXPLORE

Find more friends

Photos

4 Albums

©MGA

DJ Dylan! LOL

©MGA

Rock Angelz Latest Concert Pics

©MGA

Stilesville Snaps

©MGA

New York Trip

Profile

©MGA

Sasha™

Today I'm: organising my desk.

Hometown: Stilesville

School: Stiles High

Activities: Planning the hottest gigs in Stilesville, spending time with my BFFs.

Interests: Music, fashion, the perfect wardrobe organisation plan (kidding, you girls!).

Favourite music: Beyoncé's super-stylin, but I love any new, fresh music that sounds awesome.

Favourite books: Autobiographies of the super-successful.

Notice Board

Show All | **Today** | Yesterday | Last Week

Displaying 1–5 of 261 notices.

At 6:04pm yesterday **Yasmin** said
Come on girl, forget the desk tidying and come and eat cupcakes!

At 2:18pm yesterday **Felicia** said
With that music, this is gonna be the best girls' night out ever!

At 1:54pm yesterday **Maribel** said
Are you going to Dana's sleepover on the 15th?

At 12:14pm yesterday **Roxxi** said
Did you check out that demo tape?

At 10:58am yesterday **Jade** said
That'd be awesome, Bunny Boo – thanks!

FORUM GROUPS CREATE

Friends

Mutual | See All | Groups | Find New

 **Cameron** is thinking about a certain someone . . .

 **Cloe** is lazing in the sun and catching up on some reading . . . my fave celebrity mags!

 **Dana** is enjoying my strawberry smoothie.

 **Dylan** is mainly thinking about food.

 **Felicia** is looking forward to a girls' night out!

 **Fianna** is such a sleepyhead today!

 **Jade** is checking out the new fashion boutique in the mall.

 **Katia** is back in Stilesville on Monday – yay!

 **Kumi** can't wait to get the photos developed!

 **Maribel** is looking forward to the weekend.

 **Meygan** is giving in to temptation – those cupcakes are irresistible!

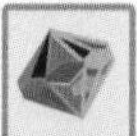 **Nevra** is about to go to dance class.

 **Phoebe** is having a bad hair day – help me, girls!

 **Roxxi** is losing my voice – sympathy required!

 **Siernna** is making like Cloe and turning my nails into works of art!

 **Vinessa** is tired of homework!

 **Yasmin** is looking after an adorable tabby kitten.

Groups

Stiles High Girls with a passion for fashion!

Yasmin's Charity Run Fun

Stilesville's Top DJs

We Went to Stilesville Elementary School

The Movie Club

Sasha's Inside Music Tips

Latest News

Sasha wrote on **Yasmin's** notice board. 6:05pm

Sasha wrote on **Cloe's** notice board. 5:54pm

Sasha is organising my desk. 4:37pm

Sasha wrote on **Felicia's** notice board. 2:10pm

Sasha wrote on **Meribel's** notice board. 2:05pm

Sasha joined the group **Yasmin's** Charity Run Fund. 12:40pm

Sasha wrote on **Roxxi's** notice board. 12:26pm

Sasha wrote on **Jade's** notice board. 11:23am

http://www.myprofile.com/allaboutyou

HOME | ABOUT YOU | EXPLORE

Search

Find more friends

Messages

Photos

Fun Stuff

Groups

Profile

Stick Your Photo Here

Name:

Today I'm:

Hometown:

School:

Activities:

Interests:

Favourite music:

Favourite books:

FORUM GROUPS CREATE

X Friends

Mutual | See All | Groups | Find New

Write a few lines about each of your BFFs!

1.

2.

3.

4.

5.

– Music

– Birthdays

X Latest News

WEIRD WORDSEARCH

Check out this super-sized wordsearch. There are thirteen (unlucky for some!) spooky words hidden in the grid – can you find them all?

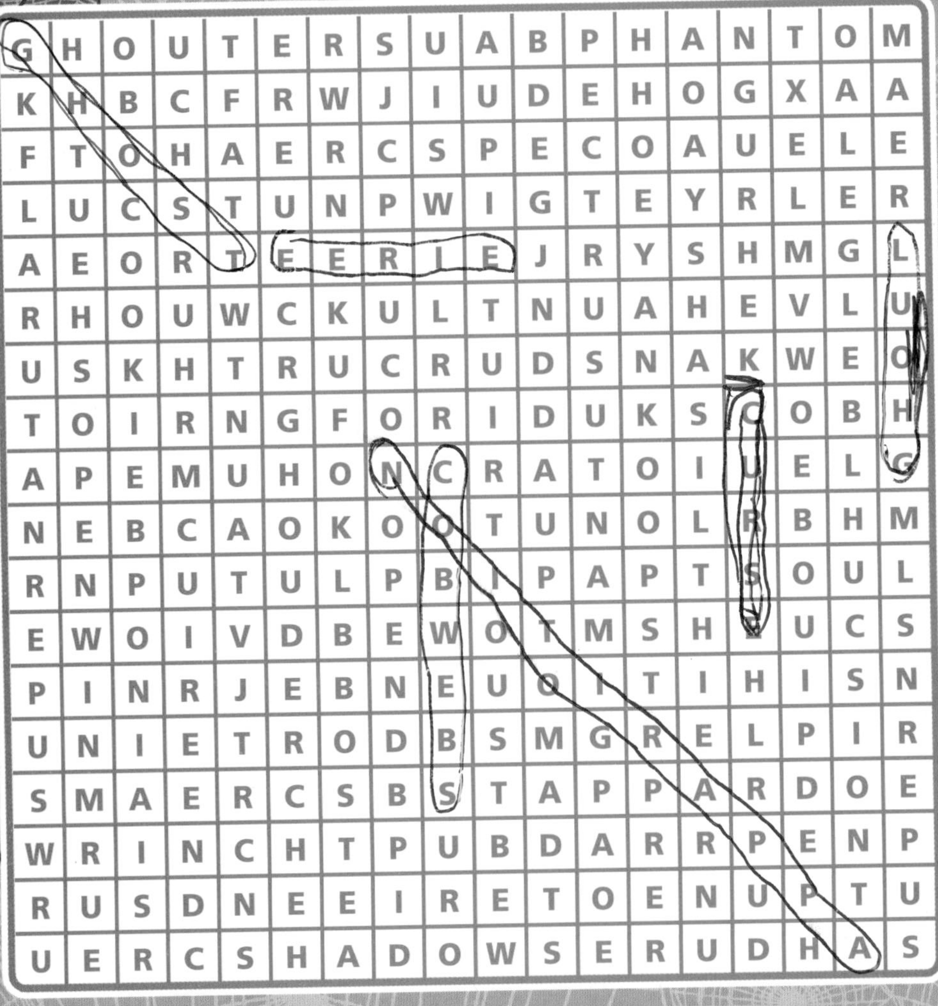

G	H	O	U	T	E	R	S	U	A	B	P	H	A	N	T	O	M
K	H	B	C	F	R	W	J	I	U	D	E	H	O	G	X	A	A
F	T	O	H	A	E	R	C	S	P	E	C	O	A	U	E	L	E
L	U	C	S	T	U	N	P	W	I	G	T	E	Y	R	L	E	R
A	E	O	R	T	E	E	R	I	E	J	R	Y	S	H	M	G	L
R	H	O	U	W	C	K	U	L	T	N	U	A	H	E	V	L	U
U	S	K	H	T	R	U	C	R	U	D	S	N	A	K	W	E	O
T	O	I	R	N	G	F	O	R	I	D	U	K	S	C	O	B	H
A	P	E	M	U	H	O	N	C	R	A	T	O	I	U	E	L	G
N	E	B	C	A	O	K	O	O	T	U	N	O	L	R	B	H	M
R	N	P	U	T	U	L	P	B	I	P	A	P	T	S	O	U	L
E	W	O	I	V	D	B	E	W	O	T	M	S	H	E	U	C	S
P	I	N	R	J	E	B	N	E	U	O	I	T	I	H	I	S	N
U	N	I	E	T	R	O	D	B	S	M	G	R	E	L	P	I	R
S	M	A	E	R	C	S	B	S	T	A	P	P	A	R	D	O	E
W	R	I	N	C	H	T	P	U	B	D	A	R	R	P	E	N	P
R	U	S	D	N	E	E	I	R	E	T	O	E	N	U	P	T	U
U	E	R	C	S	H	A	D	O	W	S	E	R	U	D	H	A	S

- APPARITION
- COBWEBS
- CURSE
- EERIE
- GHOST
- GHOUL
- HAUNT
- PHANTOM
- SCREAM
- SHADOWS
- SPECTRE
- SPOOK
- SUPERNATURAL

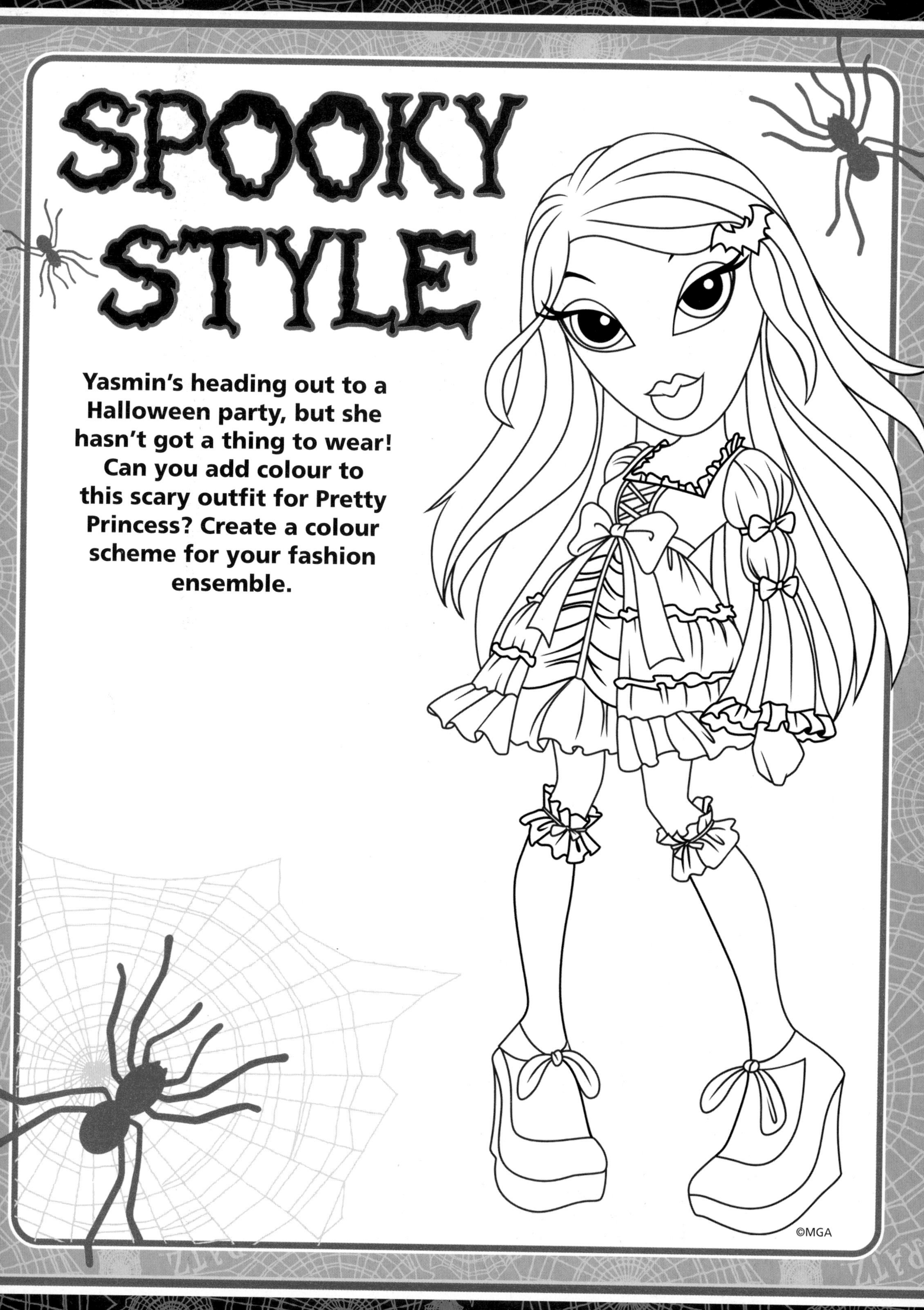

SPOOKY STYLE

Yasmin's heading out to a Halloween party, but she hasn't got a thing to wear! Can you add colour to this scary outfit for Pretty Princess? Create a colour scheme for your fashion ensemble.

Yasmin's Guide To Writing Poetry

I love writing stories, but if you really want to conjure up a mood in seconds, poetry is the best way. Poems can be funny, scary, silly or sad – they can make people laugh or cry. You can express your feelings in just a few lines of poetry – it can be better than keeping a diary! Check out my guide to writing poems and see what you can create!

Rhyming Poems

Lots of people love rhyming poems. Rhymes can be lots of fun, and they are especially good for funny poems.

Free Verse

If you write in free verse, it means that you don't have to make your poem rhyme. Instead, think about the rhythm of the poem. Is it easy to read aloud? The words should flow and not make you stumble.

Funny Poem

1. Write down the name of your best friend.

2. Now write down some words that describe what she looks like.

3. Finally, write some words that describe her personality.

4. Use a rhyming dictionary (check out the internet) to write down words that rhyme with the list of words above.

5. Now write an eight-line rhyming poem describing your friend! Here's one I wrote about Cloe, to give you some ideas.

***Her hair's the colour of the sun,
Our drama mama's full of fun.
Art is in her fingertips
And laughter's always on her lips.
Her eyes are like a summer sky.
(They shine when Cameron passes by!)
Our Angel's sweet and kind and clever.
We know we'll be best friends forever!***

Scary Poem

1. Write down three things that scare you.

----

2. Now think of a time when you were really scared. What happened?

----

3. Grab a thesaurus and look up some scary words. You'll discover lots more that you can use in your poem. Find some really exciting, chilling words!

----

4. With this poem, your aim is to make your reader feel what you felt! It is going to be written in free verse. If you are thinking about making words rhyme, you won't be able to concentrate on making your poem really scary! Tell the story of what happened to you as if it is happening as you write. For example:

I walk down the cold, misty path.
Fog curls around me like soft fingers
covering my eyes.
A gate creaks.

Try to tell the story in ten lines. Describe what happened using powerful, descriptive words. Scare your reader!

Emotional Poem

1. In the first space write an emotion.

2. In the second space write the name of a job title.

3. Then think about what would make that sort of person have that sort of feeling, and write it in the final space.

4. You can do the same thing over and over again. Try using animal names or places in the second space. This is the start of your poem - what will you write next?

I've given some examples to help you out:

I'm as sad as a singer with no song to sing.

I'm as happy as a butterfly that's unfurling its new wings in the sun.

I'm as lonely as a beach in the depths of winter.

5. Now it's your turn!

I'm as ____________________

as a ____________________

in ____________________.

I'm as ____________________

as a ____________________

with ____________________.

I'm as ____________________

as a ____________________

that's ____________________.

HALLOWEEN PARTY PLANNER

Compile guest list.

Visit the venue and make a plan of the space. Make a note of the furniture that is already there. Check that there is somewhere for the band or the sound system.

13

Don't forget about your own costume! Plan your outfit or costume and scope out some awesome accessories. Make sure you know how you are going to do your hair, and what shoes and bag you are going to wear.

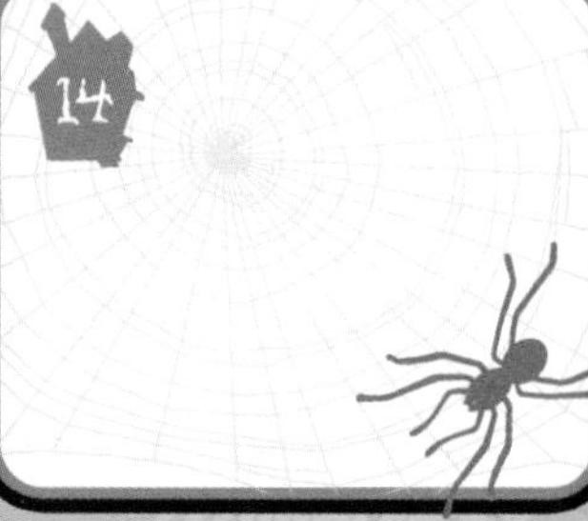

19

Spend a day making a list of all the food and drink you'll need. (You can only do this when you know how many guests you will have.) Don't plan too many foods that you have to cook from scratch!

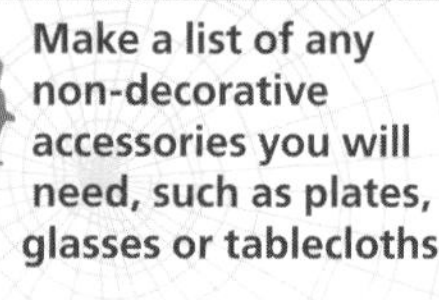

Make a list of any non-decorative accessories you will need, such as plates, glasses or tablecloths.

Check through your mix CDs and make sure that you have enough music to last all night

For a terrifyingly good Halloween party, you need to plan well in advance. There are lots of things to organise, but if you follow our party planner, you'll be totally on top of the situation and you'll throw a party that'll never be forgotten!

2 Decide on party venue. Do you have to book in advance? Check that it is available on the 31st!

3 If you're going to have a live band, now's the time to book them. If you're using your own music, start creating mix CDs to get everyone dancing!

4 Design and send invitations. Remember to tell guests the venue, date and time, and whether the party is fancy dress!

5

9 Design a fabulous look for the party and make a list of any accessories or decoration you will need, such as fabric, flowers, pumpkins or fake cobwebs!

10

11 Hit the shops! Buy all the items on your list and make sure that you have everything you will need to create the party that you have imagined.

12

15 Check replies to invitations and tick off against guest list. Follow up any guests who have not replied.

16

17 Plan some fun party games to get everyone relaxed and full of party spirit!

18

22

23 Time to go shopping again! This time you should buy all the food, drink and accessories you'll need, including anything that you can store in the freezer.

24

25 Check that you have everything you will need for the party games, and prepare any props.

29

30 Hit the shops for the food and decoration items that have to be fresh, such as cakes and flowers. Prepare the food and drinks.

31 Get up early and decorate the party venue. Lay out the plates, glasses, food and drinks. Have a long, hot soak in the bath and then get into your outfit. Party!

1

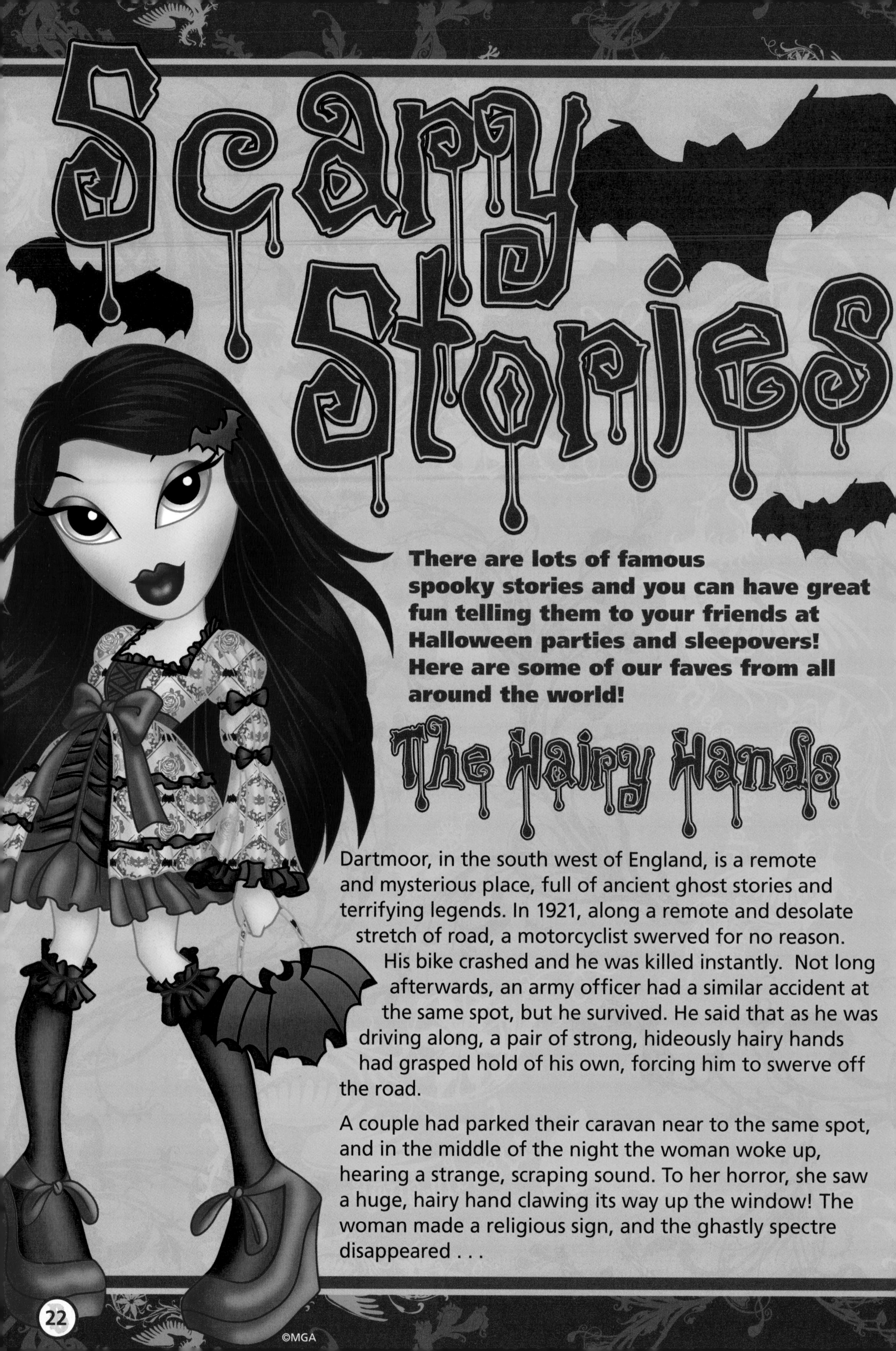

Scary Stories

There are lots of famous spooky stories and you can have great fun telling them to your friends at Halloween parties and sleepovers! Here are some of our faves from all around the world!

The Hairy Hands

Dartmoor, in the south west of England, is a remote and mysterious place, full of ancient ghost stories and terrifying legends. In 1921, along a remote and desolate stretch of road, a motorcyclist swerved for no reason. His bike crashed and he was killed instantly. Not long afterwards, an army officer had a similar accident at the same spot, but he survived. He said that as he was driving along, a pair of strong, hideously hairy hands had grasped hold of his own, forcing him to swerve off the road.

A couple had parked their caravan near to the same spot, and in the middle of the night the woman woke up, hearing a strange, scraping sound. To her horror, she saw a huge, hairy hand clawing its way up the window! The woman made a religious sign, and the ghastly spectre disappeared . . .

Silver Heels

In Colorado, America, there are many small towns that were created during the Gold Rush, when gold was found in nearby rivers. In 1861, an exquisitely beautiful dancer came to dance in one of the mining camp towns. No one knew her real name – thanks to her enchanting dancing, she was only known as 'Silver Heels'.

That winter, the deadly smallpox disease infected the mining camp. It swept through the town, striking down the miners and their families. Many people died, and there were no nurses. Silver Heels did everything she could to help. She stayed in cabin after cabin, nursing those who were ill, caring for the families and burying the dead.

When the epidemic was over, the miners realised that their beloved Silver Heels had vanished. She had not left by horse or carriage, but her cabin was empty. They searched the mountains for her, but found nothing.

Some said that she had contracted smallpox, which had left her once-lovely face horribly scarred, and that she had run away. However, others said that she never left the little town. Over the years, several people have seen the ghostly form of a heavily veiled woman in the graveyard, dressed all in black and carrying flowers. If she is approached, she simply vanishes into the mountain mists.

Australia's Most Haunted House

In Monte Cristo, Australia, there is a large house with wide verandas, beautiful gardens . . . and at least ten different ghosts. The house was first owned in 1884 by the Crawley family, and the spirit of old Mrs Crawley has been seen many times in her old room.

Late one night, a visitor and his girlfriend were walking through the hall when they heard a voice from the top of the dark stairs. When they looked up, they saw a young woman all in white. She said softly, "Don't worry, it will be all right," and then vanished before their eyes.

The family living there often heard footsteps when they were alone in the house, and sometimes saw mysterious lights flickering when they came home, although the house should have been dark and unlit.

One room of the house has been the scene of countless ghostly experiences. People staying in the room have reported phantom faces at the window, floating apparitions in the room and a bodiless face appearing at the foot of the bed.

Many visitors have reported seeing ghostly children in the grounds of the house, including a boy dressed in a sailor suit, who is always seen in or near a tree. Records show that several children died in Monte Cristo in the 19th century . . .

Yasmin and the Haunted House

I was walking through a dark, cold room, cobwebs brushing against my face. Something up ahead of me was glimmering – a single candle in the dark. I moved slowly towards it, holding my hands out in front of me. When I reached the candle, I realised that it was floating in the air, with no hand to hold it up! Then I saw a mirror in front of me. I drew closer and peered at my outfit.

I was wearing a faux layered double tank tunic top with printed leggings and a colour-stained denim mini-skirt. Brightly coloured charm bracelets dangled from my wrists and reflective trims on my clothing glinted in the candlelight. It was a totally awesome, completely mind-blowing outfit! I was so entranced that I forgot about the dark room behind me, I didn't hear the heavy, shuffling steps until it was too late, and a hairy hand slammed down on my shoulder!

"AAAGGGHHH!" I screamed, and sat bolt upright in bed.

"Murder!" hollered Cloe, burrowing down into her sleeping bag.

"I'll get them!" yelled Sasha in a fury.

"What's going on?" said Jade, stifling a huge yawn.

We had stayed up late discussing our outfits for Cameron's Halloween party, but we hadn't come up with anything super-inspired. However, my brain must have been working on it in my sleep . . .

"You guys, I have just dreamed up the best new look *ever*!" I said.

"Did you have to terrify us to tell us about it?" enquired Sasha, dropping back with her hand over her heart.

"Didn't scare me," grinned Jade, stretching and yawning.

Cloe was still squeaking around at the bottom of her sleeping bag.

"I'm sorry, Bunny Boo," I said with a laugh, hopping out of bed. "But Kool Kat, even you are going to flip out over this new look!"

As evening drew in around us, Cloe led the way down Spooks Lane, following the map Cameron had drawn for her.

"Spooks Lane is the perfect place for a Halloween party, isn't it!" I said, shivering as the fog drifted around us.

"Yeess," said Cloe, sounding rather uncertain. "I think I would have preferred it to be in the centre of Stilesville. This is kind of creepy."

"Cameron said that hardly anyone lives down here," Jade added, looking around. "I guess he's right!"

The girls were completely besotted with the outfit I had seen in my dream. When Cloe finally emerged from her sleeping bag, we got dressed and set off for the mall. We had an awesome day picking out the perfect outfits, and by the time we set out for the party, we were looking as spectacular as any fashionista could wish.

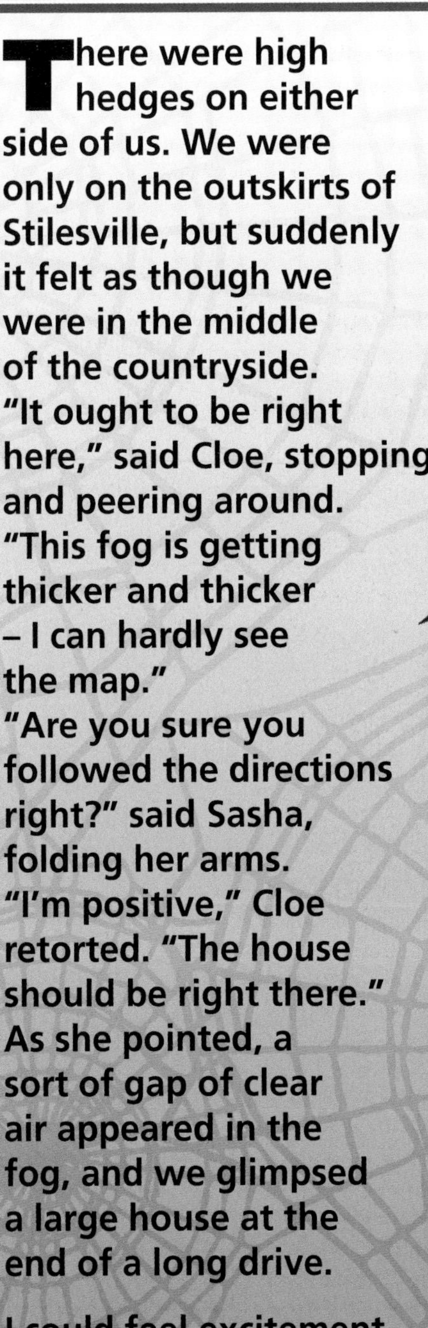

There were high hedges on either side of us. We were only on the outskirts of Stilesville, but suddenly it felt as though we were in the middle of the countryside.

"It ought to be right here," said Cloe, stopping and peering around. "This fog is getting thicker and thicker – I can hardly see the map."

"Are you sure you followed the directions right?" said Sasha, folding her arms.

"I'm positive," Cloe retorted. "The house should be right there."

As she pointed, a sort of gap of clear air appeared in the fog, and we glimpsed a large house at the end of a long drive.

I could feel excitement bubbling inside me at the thought of the party – with such a grand setting, it was sure to be fantastic! But as we hurried up the drive, a little doubt crept into my mind. We were already a few minutes late, and yet the house looked kind of . . . *empty*.

There were no lights in the windows and no cars in the drive. I paused and grabbed Sasha's arm. "Er, are we sure this is the right place?" I said. "There are no lights."

"It must be," said Sasha. "Cameron said it's the only house at this end of Spooks Lane."

At that moment we saw a light flickering in an upstairs room. It looked like a candle, and a shiver suddenly ran through me. In the fun of choosing our outfits I had forgotten about the rest of my dream, but now it all came back to me. It was as if I could still feel the weight of that hairy hand on my shoulder . . .

"Have you turned to stone?" said Cloe. "Come on, girl!"

I hurried after my friends. By the time I joined them at the huge main entrance, Sasha had already rung the bell. It resounded around the house like a gong.

I peered through the frosted glass panes in the huge front door. Sasha reached out and turned the marble doorknob, and the door swung open with a loud creak.

"Sasha!" I protested. "We can't just walk in!"

"It's a party," said Sasha. "The music's probably so loud that they can't hear the doorbell."

We followed Sasha and I shut the door behind me. We were standing in a large entrance hall, with a wide staircase spiralling up to the first floor.

"I can't hear any music," said Cloe, sounding uneasy.

"Let's go on a party hunt then," said Jade.

"But it's really d-dark," Cloe objected.

As she spoke, a cold draught blew through the hall and half opened the door of a room to our left. A golden glow came from inside.

"Must be through here," said Sasha.

She strode through the door . . . and then we heard her shriek.

We raced into the room and suddenly I felt something cold groping at my face! I screamed, fighting it off. Cloe screamed too, but Jade was laughing. "Will you three calm down?" she said. "It's just cobwebs." Feeling rather embarrassed, I wiped the sticky webs from my face and hair, and looked around the room. Everything was covered in a thick layer of dust and cobwebs. Everything except . . .

"The f-fire," said Cloe, pointing a shaking finger. "Someone's lit a fire." A fire was burning hungrily in the grate. We stared at each other, our faces looking strangely unfamiliar in the flickering light. "Well," said Sasha after a long pause. "That just proves there's someone here." "Why would they have lit a fire but not cleaned the room?" I asked. "There's bound be a perfectly logical explanation," Jade said. "After all, it's a Halloween party. They're probably *trying* to scare us."

At that moment there was a sound from above. It sounded like a step. We all froze and looked up. The fire seemed to die away slightly. "They must be upstairs," said Sasha. But her voice wavered. There was another footstep above, and Sasha took a deep breath. "Come on," she said. "We'll all go up. There's obviously someone up there – it's probably Dylan messing around." We walked out of the sitting room and back into the hall. Moonlight was shining through a window at the top of the staircase, illuminating the stairs. Without saying a word, we linked hands and walked up the wide, grand staircase. At the top was a long corridor, with many doors along it. The first door was slightly open, and we heard a footstep inside. Sasha strode forward and burst into the room. We were all close behind her. I glanced around as fast as I could, but there was no one in there.

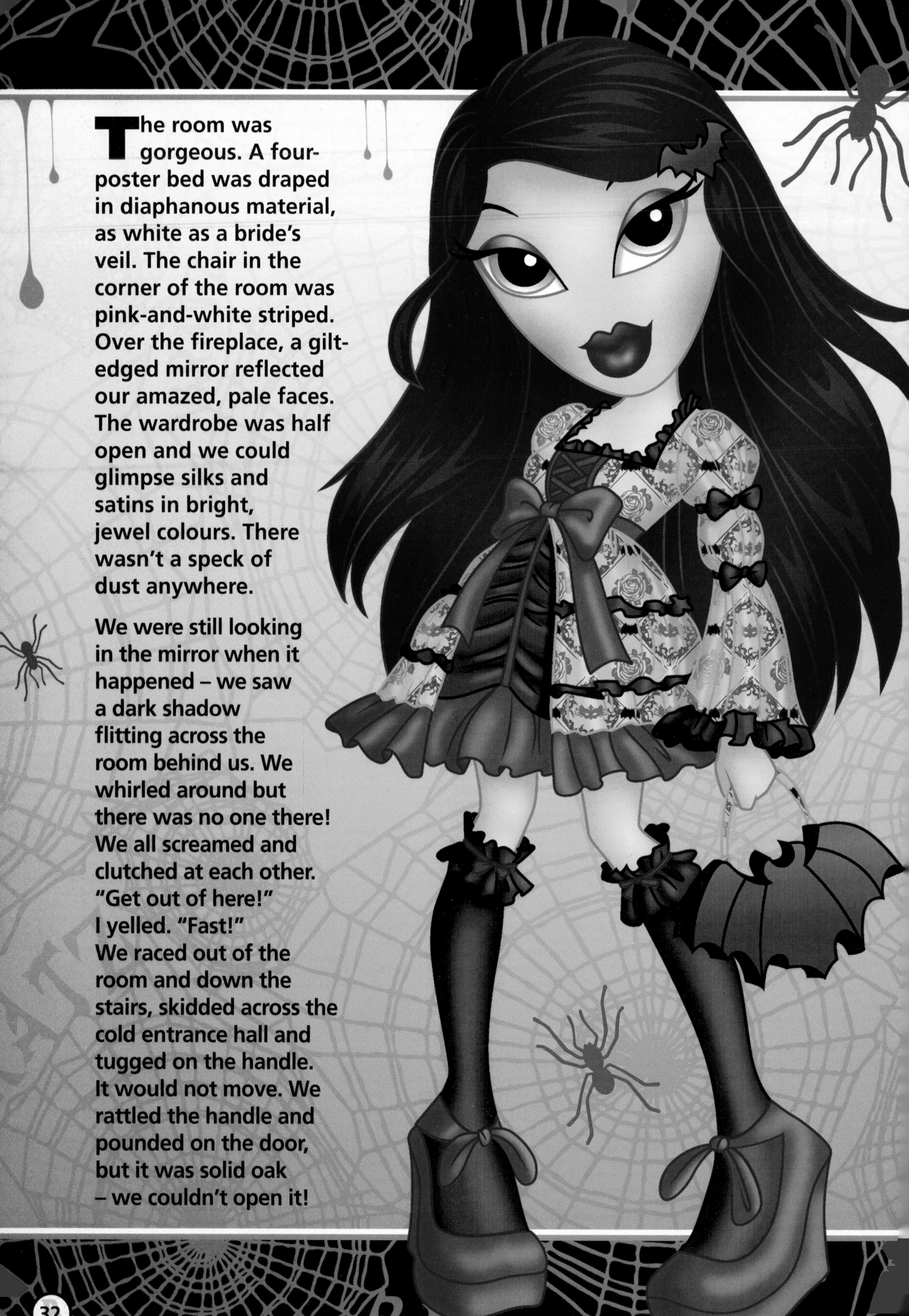

The room was gorgeous. A four-poster bed was draped in diaphanous material, as white as a bride's veil. The chair in the corner of the room was pink-and-white striped. Over the fireplace, a gilt-edged mirror reflected our amazed, pale faces. The wardrobe was half open and we could glimpse silks and satins in bright, jewel colours. There wasn't a speck of dust anywhere.

We were still looking in the mirror when it happened – we saw a dark shadow flitting across the room behind us. We whirled around but there was no one there! We all screamed and clutched at each other. "Get out of here!" I yelled. "Fast!" We raced out of the room and down the stairs, skidded across the cold entrance hall and tugged on the handle. It would not move. We rattled the handle and pounded on the door, but it was solid oak – we couldn't open it!

"We have to smash the glass!" Sasha yelled. She seized a small wooden table that was standing in the hall and raised it in the air, ready to smash the frosted glass in the front door. And that's when we saw it. A face appeared in the glass – no body, just a face – with wide, staring, dark eyes and thin lips drawn back over crooked teeth.

"AAAGGGHHH!" we all screamed together. I was frozen to the spot – even Jade looked terrified. Cloe was the first to move. "The back door!" she yelled. "We have to get out of here – now!" We raced after her as she sprinted through the dark house. She led us through an echoing, empty kitchen, sending pans and crockery flying around us. There was a small back door and Cloe skidded to a halt in front of it, fumbling with a key in the lock.

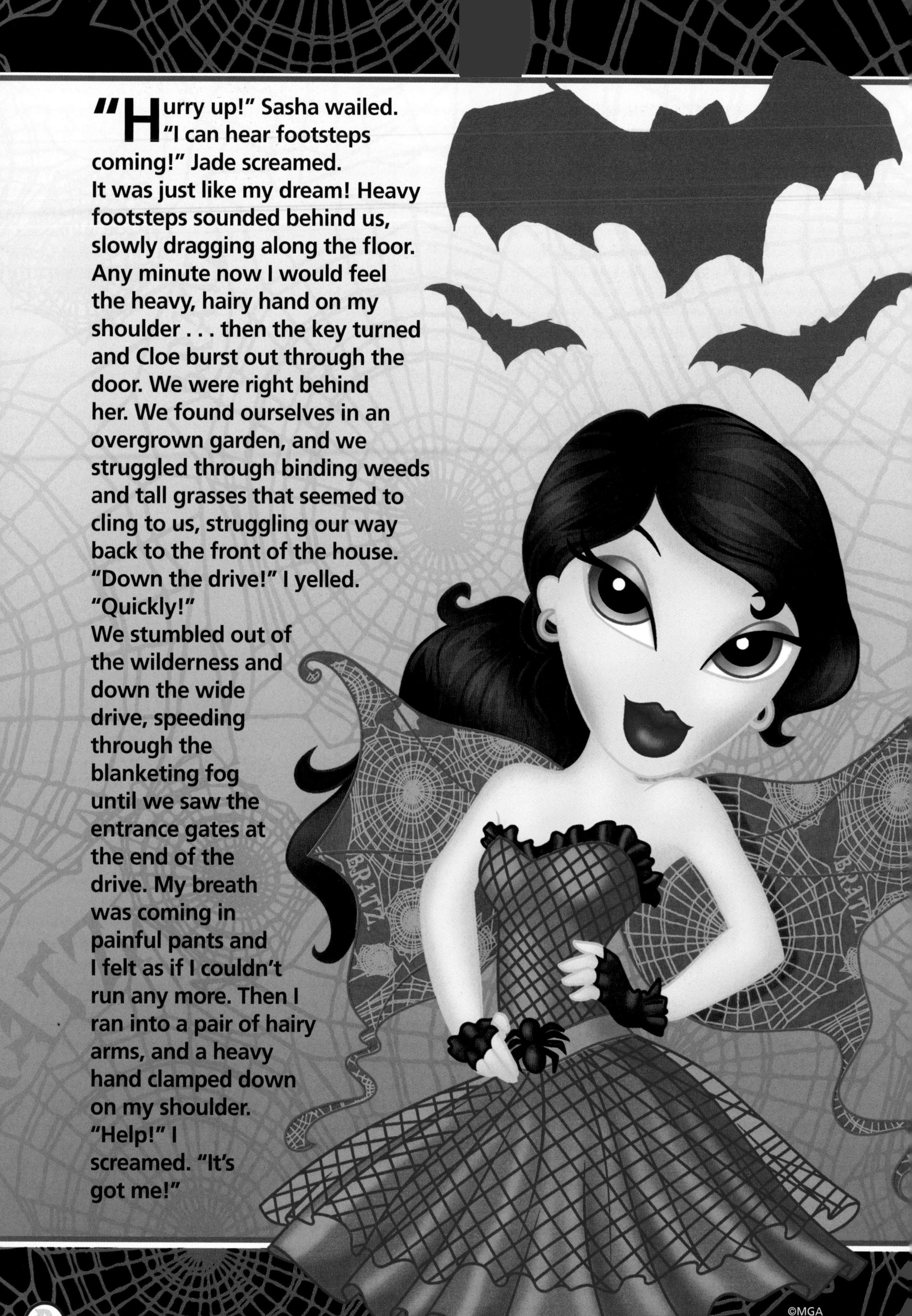

"Hurry up!" Sasha wailed. "I can hear footsteps coming!" Jade screamed.
It was just like my dream! Heavy footsteps sounded behind us, slowly dragging along the floor. Any minute now I would feel the heavy, hairy hand on my shoulder . . . then the key turned and Cloe burst out through the door. We were right behind her. We found ourselves in an overgrown garden, and we struggled through binding weeds and tall grasses that seemed to cling to us, struggling our way back to the front of the house.
"Down the drive!" I yelled. "Quickly!"
We stumbled out of the wilderness and down the wide drive, speeding through the blanketing fog until we saw the entrance gates at the end of the drive. My breath was coming in painful pants and I felt as if I couldn't run any more. Then I ran into a pair of hairy arms, and a heavy hand clamped down on my shoulder.
"Help!" I screamed. "It's got me!"

"Keep quiet, silly!" said the monster in a familiar voice. It removed its head . . . to reveal Dylan's grinning face.

"What are you doing here?" asked Cameron, who was dressed as a vampire. "The party's at the other end of the lane."

We gaped at him.

"So we just . . . *broke in* . . . to that *haunted* house," said Cloe. "No wonder the ghosts had it in for us!"

"What haunted house?" said Cameron, looking bewildered.

"That one!" said Sasha, pointing towards the house . . .

But the house wasn't there. The fog had cleared, the moon was bright, and there was no house in sight.

"That's . . . not . . . possible," said Sasha.

"But we were *inside*," said Cloe in shock.

"Maybe you've seen Halloween House!" said Cameron. "It's an old Stilesville legend. It appears for an hour each Halloween. And if anyone goes inside . . ."

"They're never seen again," finished Dylan. "I know the whole story, if you want to hear it?"

"You know what?" said Sasha. "I really, *really* don't."

I took a deep breath and decided to go and enjoy the party. Maybe our imaginations got the better of us.

But I'm never going down Spooks Lane at Halloween again!

HOROSCOPES

ARIES
20 Mar - 20 Apr
Good qualities: Active, leader, independent, assertive.
Negative tendencies: Impatient, aggressive, naïve.
Best friendship match: Aquarius, Libra, Gemini
Best crush match: Sagittarius, Leo.

TAURUS
21 Apr - 20 May
Good qualities: Dependable, down-to-earth, determined.
Negative tendencies: Possessive, stubborn.
Best friendship match: Cancer, Scorpio, Pisces
Best crush match: Virgo, Capricorn

GEMINI
21 May - 20 June
Good qualities: Flexible, sociable, adaptable.
Negative tendencies: Changeable, superficial.
Best friendship match: Sagittarius, Leo, Aries.
Best crush match: Aquarius, Libra.

CANCER
21 June - 21 July
Good qualities: Gentle, thoughtful, caring.
Negative tendencies: Defensive, moody.
Best friendship match: Virgo, Taurus, Capricorn
Best crush match: Scorpio, Pisces.

LEO
22 July - 22 Aug
Good qualities: Generous, caring, open.
Negative tendencies: Bossy.
Best friendship match: Gemini, Libra, Aquarius.
Best crush match: Sagittarius, Aries.

VIRGO
22 Aug - 21 Sept
Good qualities: Intelligent, helpful, conscientious.
Negative tendencies: Critical, fussy.
Best friendship match: Cancer, Pisces, Scorpio.
Best crush match: Taurus, Capricorn.

Some people believe that your date of birth decides what your personality and fate will be. Whether you believe in astrology or not, you can have a bit of fun checking out your own star sign. How accurate is yours?

LIBRA

20 Spet - 21 Oct

Good qualities: Fair, diplomatic, kind, artistic.

Negative tendencies: Indecisive.

Best friendship match: Aries, Sagittarius, Leo.

Best crush match: Gemini, Aquarius.

SCORPIO

22 Oct - 21 Nov

Good qualities: Passionate, resourceful, focused.

Negative tendencies: Possessive, probing.

Best friendship match: Capricorn, Virgo, Taurus.

Best crush match: Cancer, Pisces

SAGITTARIUS

21 Nov - 21 Dec

Good qualities: Optimistic, enthusiastic, adventurous.

Negative tendencies: Outspoken, irresponsible.

Best friendship match: Gemini, Aquarius, Libra.

Best crush match: Aries, Leo.

CAPRICORN

21 Dec - 20 jan

Good qualities: Organised, disciplined, wise, careful.

Negative tendencies: Reserved, sarcastic.

Best friendship match: Cancer, Pisces, Scorpio.

Best crush match: Taurus, Virgo.

AQUARIUS

21 Jan - 18 Feb

qualities: Independent, inventive, original, intelligent.

Negative tendencies: Detached, opinionated.

Best friendship match: Aries, Leo, Sagittarius.

Best crush match: Gemini, Libra.

PISCES

19 Feb - 20 Mar

Good qualities: Artistic, tender, sympathetic, perceptive.

Negative tendencies: Self-pitying, absent-minded.

Best friendship match: Virgo, Taurus, Capricorn.

Best crush match: Cancer, Scorpio.

CIRCUS OF COLOUR

The best way to develop the instincts and skills of a fashion designer is to keep practising! Finish this stylin' portrait of Yasmin by adding colour to her outfit.

CROSSWORD

1. □□□■□□
2. □■□□
3. □□□■□□□□□□
4. □□□□□■□□□
5. □□□□□□■□
6. □□■□□□□□
7. □■□□□
8. □□□□□■
9. □□□□■□□

Solve the circus-related clues to find the word hidden in the shaded squares.

1. The main tent at the circus. (3,3)
2. Clowns like to throw custard ____ at each other. (4)
3. The person in charge of the circus. (10)
4. The smaller acts that happen outside the main tent. (9)
5. Performers who fly and tumble high in the air. (8)
6. Horse-riding without a saddle. (8)
7. Clowns often have big, red _____. (5)
8. The traditional call to come to the circus. (4,2)
9. A very high-up swing. (7)

What's Your Perfect

Saturday?

Work through the flow-quiz to discover your perfect weekend activity.

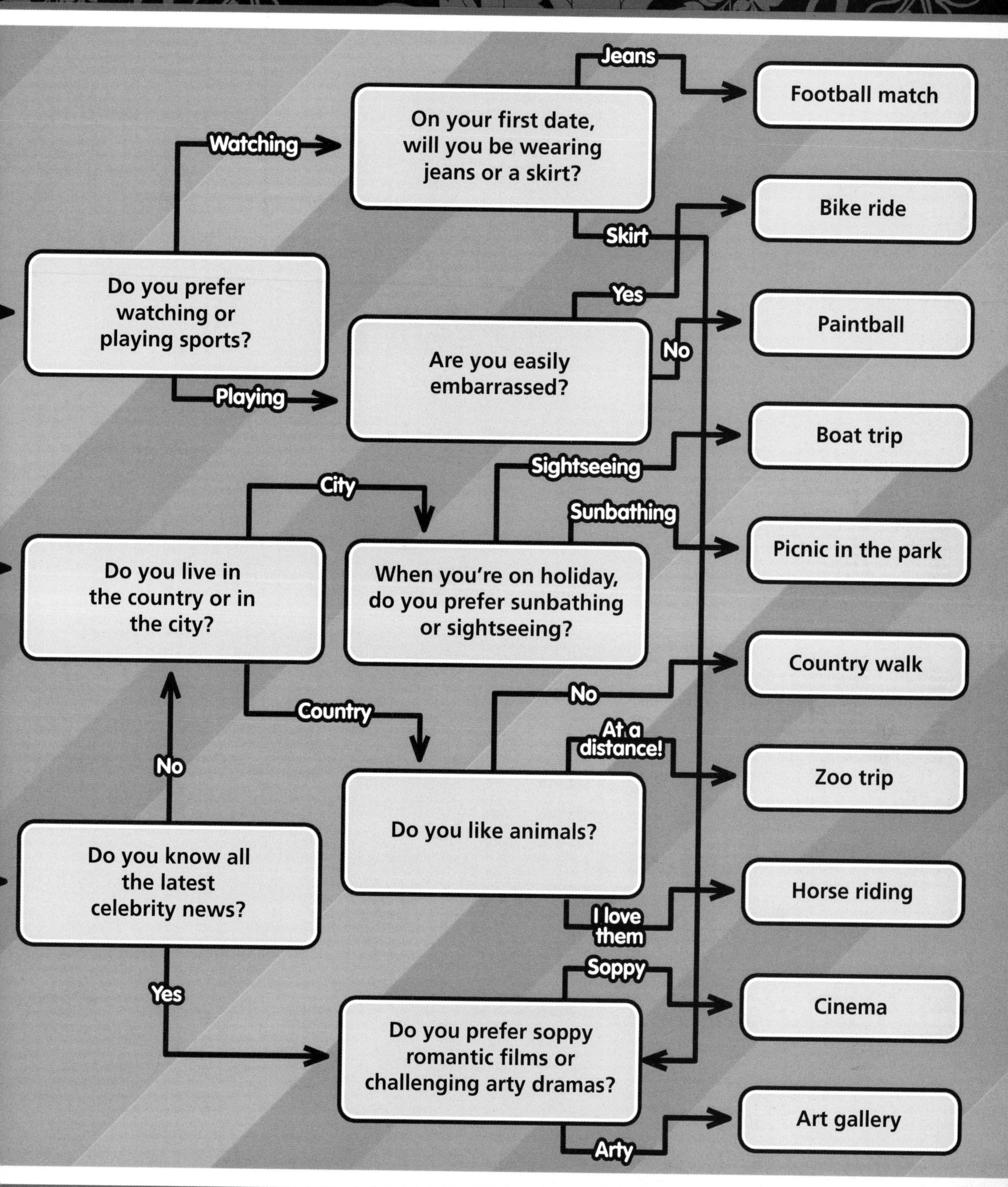

HOT NEWS

My BFFs and I have gone crazy for mineral makeup, a fantastically natural cosmetic that has been around since the funky 70s! It can protect your skin from the sun and gives your complexion a totally glowing finish, concealing any blemishes beautifully. It's great for sensitive skin, it's light and easy to apply, and best of all it's cruelty free.

SURVIVE THE PARTY SEASON

As winter comes closer, everyone's throwing a party to cheer themselves up, and you have to be seen at all the most stylin' scenes! But after a few parties, you might not be feeling so full of energy. Here are a few tips to keep you looking and feeling your best!

1. Get regular exercise. This will boost you energy levels, keep you fit, and give you a glowing, healthy look.
2. Avoid too many party snacks. They may be delicious, but too much junk food will just make you feel ill in the end.
3. Drink water. All that dancing will dehydrate you, so make sure you drink plenty of aqua!
4. Remove your makeup. At the end of the party, don't just crash! Use cleansing cloths to clean your pores and keep your face blemish free.

NATURAL AND GORGEOUS

Did you know that there are some fabulous hair treatments lurking in your kitchen cupboards?

1. For a simple conditioning treatment, rinse your hair in cider vinegar once a week. Use half a cup of vinegar mixed with half a cup of water. Shampoo and rinse your hair, then pour on the vinegar mixture. Rinse it out after a minute.
2. Olive oil can make your hair silky and shiny, help get rid of dandruff and strengthen split ends. Massage three tablespoons of olive oil into your scalp and hair. Leave it in for half an hour and then rinse.
3. For oily hair, massage finely grated carrots into wet hair, leave for 15 minutes and then rinse.
4. For dry hair, massage mashed avocado into wet hair, leave for 15 minutes and then rinse.

MY FRIENDS' TOP TEN BEAUTY SECRETS

Pull your look together from head to toe with these easy beauty tips from the girls who know best.

1. Use natural tones for eyeshadow and a nude lip colour for daytime makeup.
2. Use liquid eyeliner; it will help you to better define your eyes.
3. For long-lasting lip colour, apply a sheer layer of foundation on your lips and then dust some face powder on them before colouring them.
4. To make your lips look thicker, use a lip pencil to outline just outside your natural lip line. For thinner-looking lips, draw the outline just inside the natural lip line.
5. Use gloss to make your lips appear fuller.
6. Wearing clothes that are too tight can make you look heavy, even if you are slim.
7. Put on a coat of clear nail polish before a coloured polish to keep your nails from discolouring.
8. After washing your face, rinse in cold water to close the pores and tighten the facial muscles.
9. Choose shoes that are made of natural materials to help your feet to breathe.
10. To refresh your feet, give them a peppermint foot soak and then massage them gently with a foot roller.

CIRCUS

Check out these fun circus skills! Some of them you can practise at home, but for the unicycle you'll need the proper equipment.

Would you like to join the circus?

STILTWALKING

Walking on stilts takes a lot of skill. You can make your own practice stilts to get you started!

You will need: Two large, strong tin cans • strong cord

1. Open the tins using a tin opener that doesn't leave a sharp edge.
2. Store or eat the contents and clean the tins thoroughly.
3. Ask your 'rents to help you put a hole in each side of each tin, at the bottom (unopened) end.
4. Measure the length of your legs. Double that measurement and cut two pieces of cord to this length.
5. Thread the cord through the holes in the can and tie the two ends together so that the knot is hidden inside the tin.
6. Stand on the cans, pull up tight on the cord and practise walking on stilts!

UNICYCLE

You will need a unicycle, a helmet, some protective pads, and some heavy objects or friends to hold on to!

1. Ask two friends to stand on either side of you.
2. Get up on to the unicycle with your arms around your friends' shoulders.
3. Keep pedalling to keep your balance. Pedal half turns at first.
4. Try to keep most of your weight on the seat of the unicycle, not on the pedals.
5. Gradually lessen your hold on your friends, switching to hold their wrists and then just holding the wrist of one friend.
6. When you have been able to pedal without any support, set up a practice course with a series of objects about five feet apart. Use a friend as a back-up support if need be.

JUGGLING

Check out these exercises to help you develop your juggling skills!

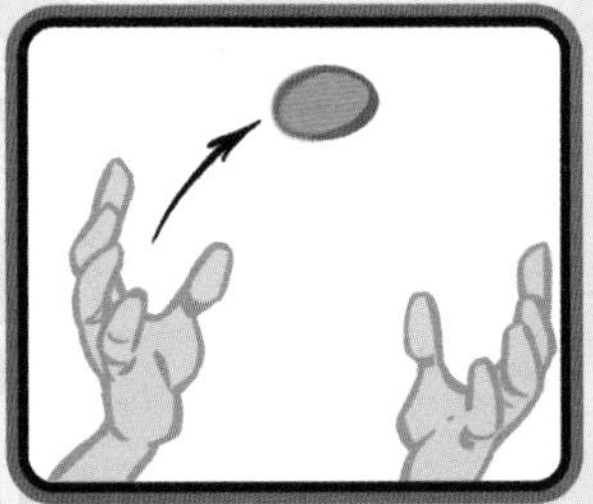

Exercise 1

Start with one ball. Throw the ball from one hand to the other at eye level. The ball should be thrown in an arc.

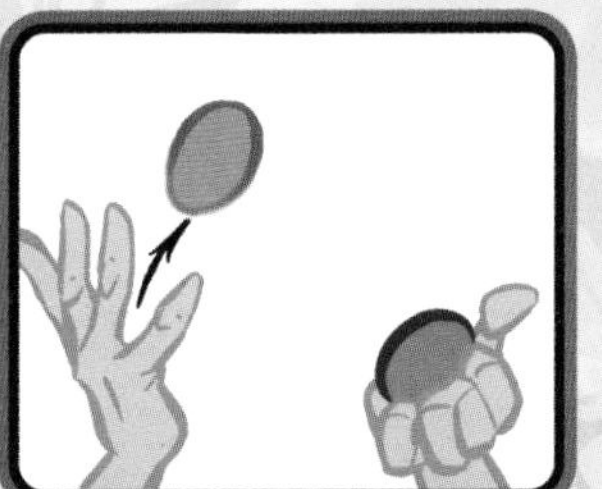

Exercise 2

Now move on to using two balls. Start with one ball in each hand.

1. First, throw the ball in your right hand in an arc to your left hand.

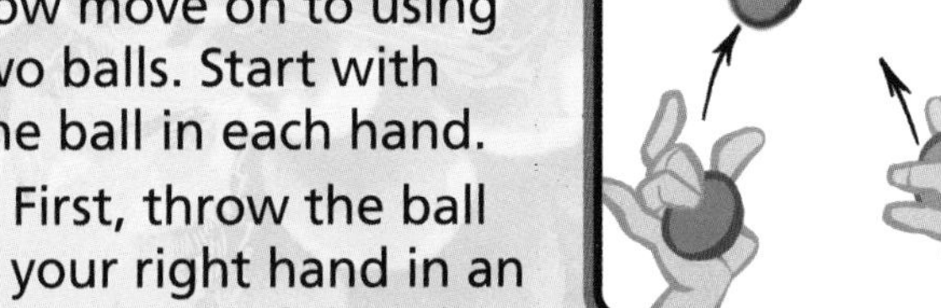

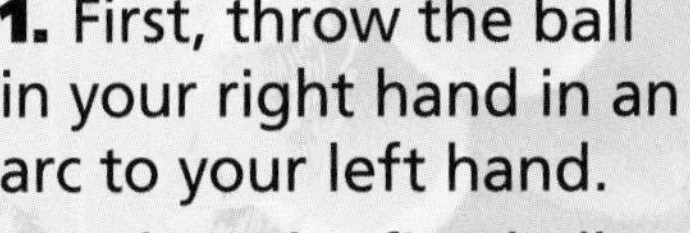

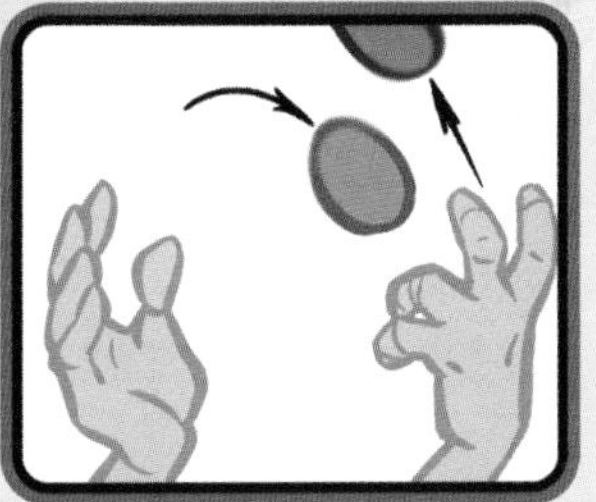

2. When the first ball reaches the highest point in its arc, throw the second ball in an arc from your left hand to your right.

3. Catch the first ball in your left hand.

4. Then catch the second ball in your right hand.

5. Repeat step 2, but this time start with the ball in your left hand.

Keep practicing until you can do this smoothly. Remember, you shouldn't throw both balls at the same time.

Exercise 3

Now you can move on to juggling three balls! Hold two balls in your right hand and one ball in your left hand.

1. First, throw one of the balls in your right hand in an arc to your left hand.

2. When the first ball reaches the highest point in its arc, throw the second ball from your left hand to your right.

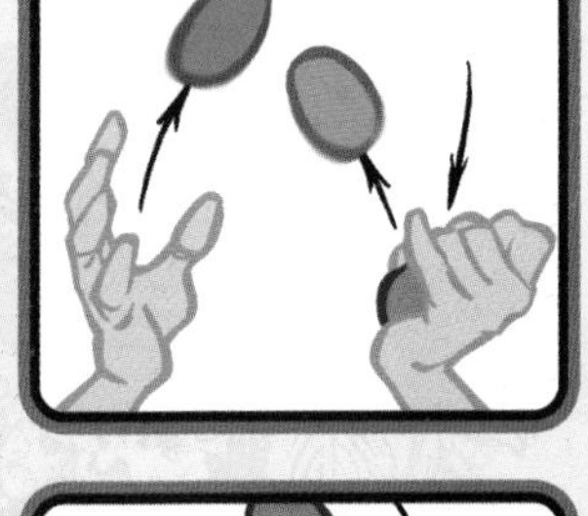

3. When the second ball reaches the highest point in its arc, catch the first ball in your left hand and throw the third ball from your right hand.

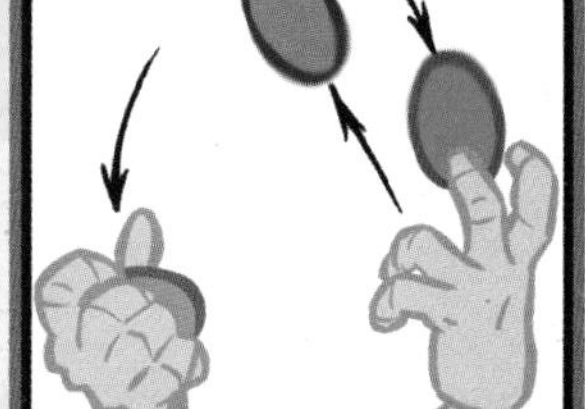

4. Catch the second ball in your right hand.

5. When the third ball reaches its highest point, throw the first ball again.

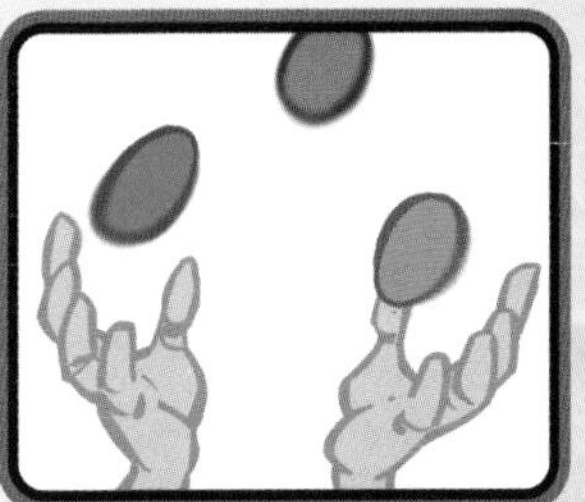

Keep practising!

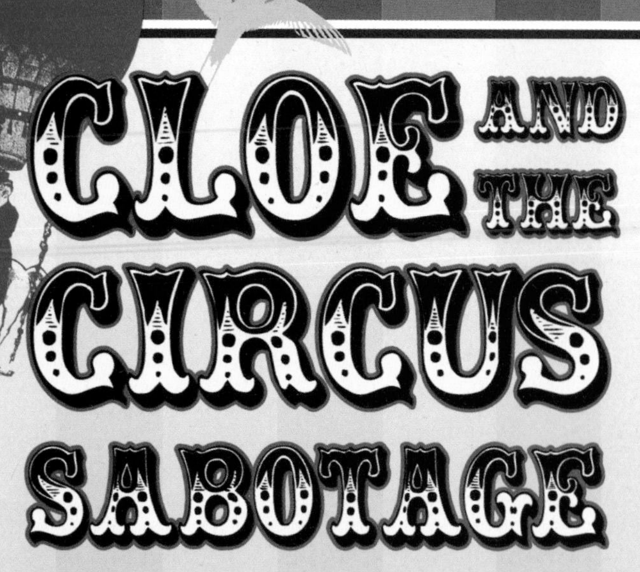

CLOE AND THE CIRCUS SABOTAGE

I looked up at the huge, candy-striped big top in the middle of the park. I could see performers in fabulous costumes strolling around, and workmen putting up the sideshows. The circus was in town, and I was super-excited! I smiled at my BFFs, Jade, Yasmin and Sasha.

"So what's the deal, Yasmin?" I asked. "Why are we several hours early for the show?"

Yasmin had texted us all and asked us to meet her in the park.

"Because I want to make sure what *kind* of show it is," said Yasmin. "Some circuses have performing animals in them, and I think that's cruel."

"Good call, Yas," said Sasha. "Let's go and find the Ringmaster and ask him. It's always best to talk to the boss."

Sasha strode into the big top. We followed her in and saw a tall, white-haired man in the middle of the sawdust-covered arena – the Ringmaster.

To our relief, the Ringmaster said that there were no animals in his show. He introduced us to some of the performers.

We met Jax the chief clown, Magnifico the fire-eater and Dazzle the bareback rider. Jax and Magnifico were really nice, but Dazzle looked a bit sulky. Just then, a man ran into the big top.
"Ringmaster, we have a problem," he said. "The Impossibles are all ill with food poisoning! They can't do the show tonight!"
The Ringmaster groaned and clapped his hand to his forehead.
"The Impossibles are our opening act," he told us. "Without them, I have nothing really explosive to open the show with!"
"I could open for you," said Jax. "I have some new –"
"No, Jax," the Ringmaster interrupted. "I need something really dazzling."
"Well, if it's dazzling you want . . ." said Dazzle, preening herself.
"You've only got one act ready," said the Ringmaster. "If I put you on first, I have an empty space in the middle of the show."
"What about me?" asked Magnifico.
"Your fire-eating is a sideshow act," the Ringmaster said.

Suddenly I had an idea. I just hoped that my BFFs would be up for it!

"What about us?" I said.

"You?" said the Ringmaster, raising his eyebrows.

"We're the Rock Angelz," I explained.

"I've heard of you," said the Ringmaster. "Yes, this could be the answer to the problem. Thank goodness you girls came along!"

"We'll have to run home and get our guitars," said Sasha.

"*And* decide what we're going to wear," Jade added.

"You mean you don't have servants to do that kind of thing for you?" Dazzle snapped. She turned and stormed out of the big top. My mouth fell open – how could anyone be so rude?

"Ignore her," said Jax. "She's been dying to open the show for ages – she's just jealous."

"I'll see you back here after lunch," said the Ringmaster. "We can go through your act then and make sure we have everything you need."

We grabbed some sandwiches for lunch and attacked our wardrobes.

"We need something that fits in with the wonder and excitement of the circus," Jade said. "Something imaginative and unconventional," Yasmin said.

"With a touch of the theatrical," I added, waving a feather boa in the air.

"And a dash of circus flair," Sasha finished, putting on a top hat and arranging it at an angle.

As soon as we had put together four fabulous circus styles, we picked up our guitars and headed back to the circus to practise.

When we arrived in the big top, it was empty. "They must all still be at lunch," said Sasha. "Hey, look over here." On a small table at the side of the arena were four glasses filled with sparkling red pop. "There's a note," I said, picking up the piece of paper next to the drinks.

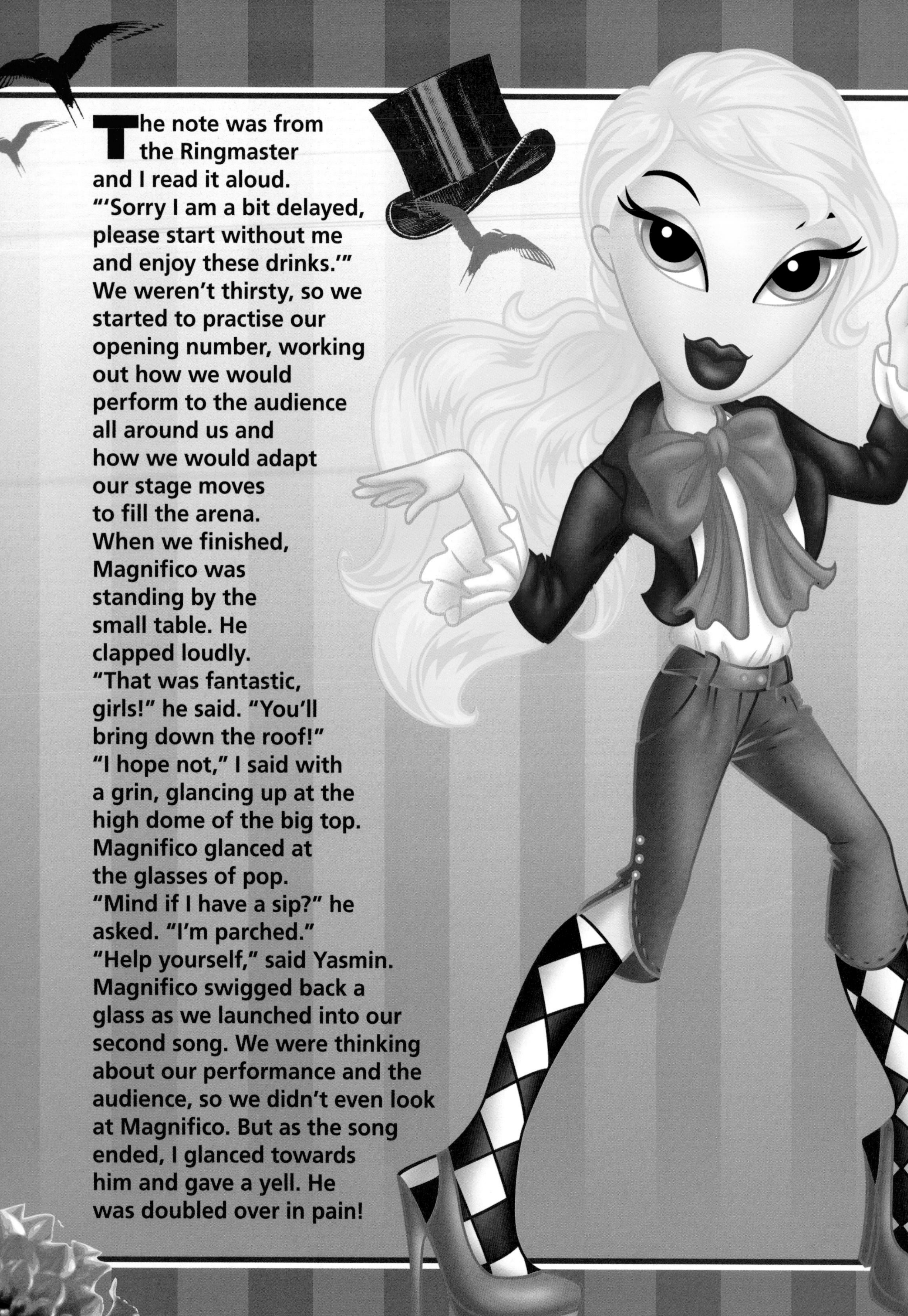

The note was from the Ringmaster and I read it aloud. "'Sorry I am a bit delayed, please start without me and enjoy these drinks.'" We weren't thirsty, so we started to practise our opening number, working out how we would perform to the audience all around us and how we would adapt our stage moves to fill the arena.

When we finished, Magnifico was standing by the small table. He clapped loudly.

"That was fantastic, girls!" he said. "You'll bring down the roof!"

"I hope not," I said with a grin, glancing up at the high dome of the big top.

Magnifico glanced at the glasses of pop.

"Mind if I have a sip?" he asked. "I'm parched."

"Help yourself," said Yasmin.

Magnifico swigged back a glass as we launched into our second song. We were thinking about our performance and the audience, so we didn't even look at Magnifico. But as the song ended, I glanced towards him and gave a yell. He was doubled over in pain!

Poor Magnifico had food poisoning too! We felt sorry for him, but our pity changed to alarm when the Ringmaster said that he hadn't left the drinks for us. Someone had tried to make us ill!

"Who would do such an awful thing?" I asked.

"Someone who wants to shut the circus down?" Jade suggested.

"Or someone who wants to have the opening act," said Yasmin.

We stepped out of the tent and saw Jax juggling. He was amazing – there had to be ten different items up in the air, all different weights and sizes! He caught them expertly when he saw us and came over with a smile.

"You girls all right?" he asked.

"We're fine," I said, "but I wish we could find out who's been doing this. Did you see anyone go into the tent?

Jax shook his head.

"But I wasn't watching the tent all the time," he said. "Loads of people must have walked past it. I saw Dazzle going to feed her horse."

"Hmm, Dazzle," said Sasha. "She wasn't happy about us getting the opening spot."

"Unhappy enough for sabotage?" Yasmin wondered.

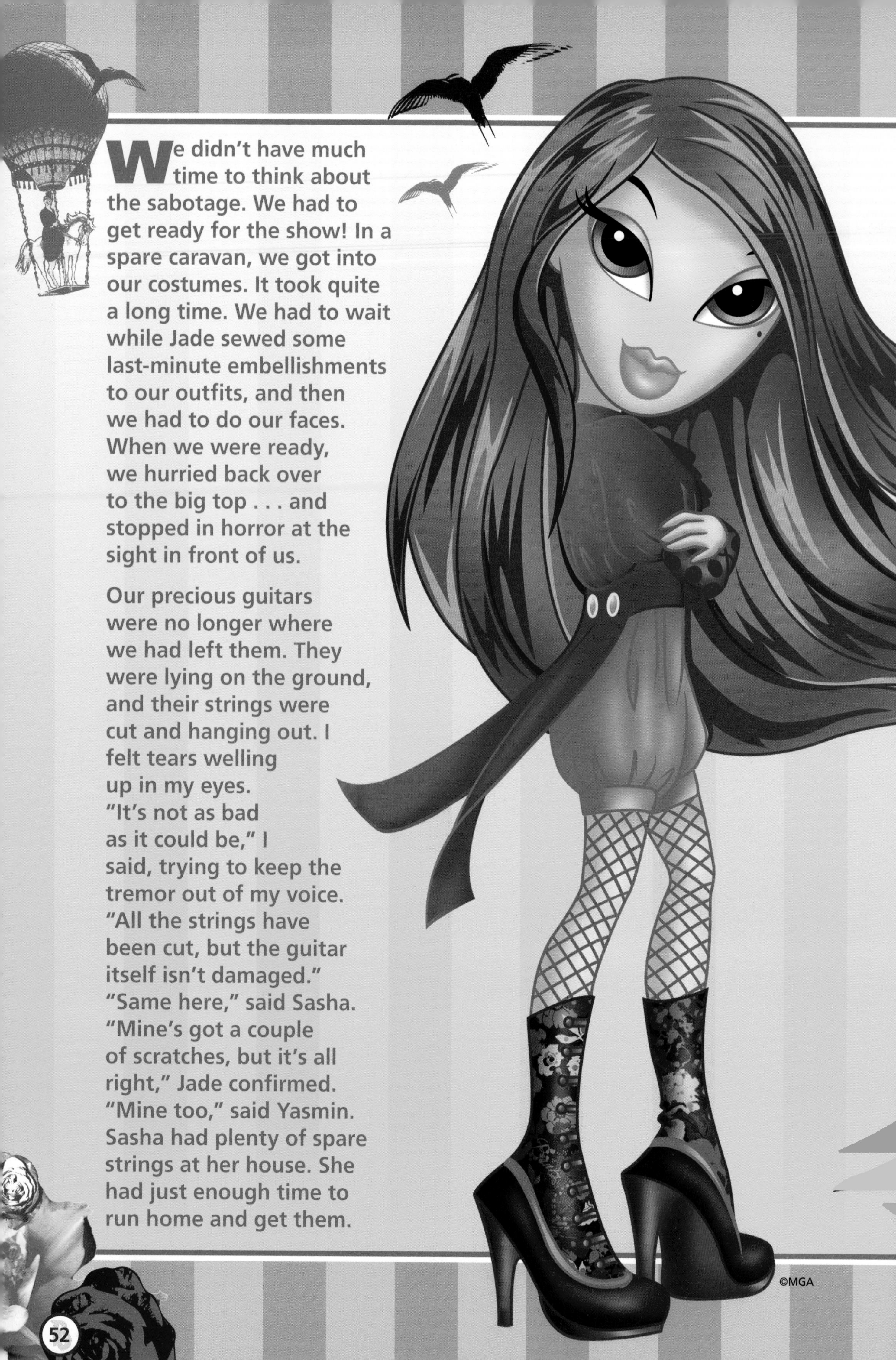

We didn't have much time to think about the sabotage. We had to get ready for the show! In a spare caravan, we got into our costumes. It took quite a long time. We had to wait while Jade sewed some last-minute embellishments to our outfits, and then we had to do our faces. When we were ready, we hurried back over to the big top . . . and stopped in horror at the sight in front of us.

Our precious guitars were no longer where we had left them. They were lying on the ground, and their strings were cut and hanging out. I felt tears welling up in my eyes.

"It's not as bad as it could be," I said, trying to keep the tremor out of my voice. "All the strings have been cut, but the guitar itself isn't damaged."

"Same here," said Sasha.

"Mine's got a couple of scratches, but it's all right," Jade confirmed.

"Mine too," said Yasmin.

Sasha had plenty of spare strings at her house. She had just enough time to run home and get them.

Cirque de Bratz

While we waited in the tent that we were using as a sort of 'backstage', other performers started to arrive in their costumes. That's when I noticed a tiny smear of red lipstick on the side of my guitar. I looked up and stared at the dancing girls who were going through their routine. Their lipstick was pink. Then I saw Dazzle walking in with a beautiful white pony. Her costume was stunning – it shone as red as rubies, with glittering sequins and a huge tail feather like a red peacock. But what really caught my attention was her scarlet lipstick.

"It's Dazzle!" I hissed in Yasmin's ear. "Look at my guitar – and look at her lipstick!"

Yasmin's mouth fell open. "She's really given herself away," she said. "No one else is wearing red lipstick. Only . . . it's a bit weird, isn't it? I mean, why would she be *kissing* your guitar?"

"I don't know," I admitted. "But it's *got* to be her."

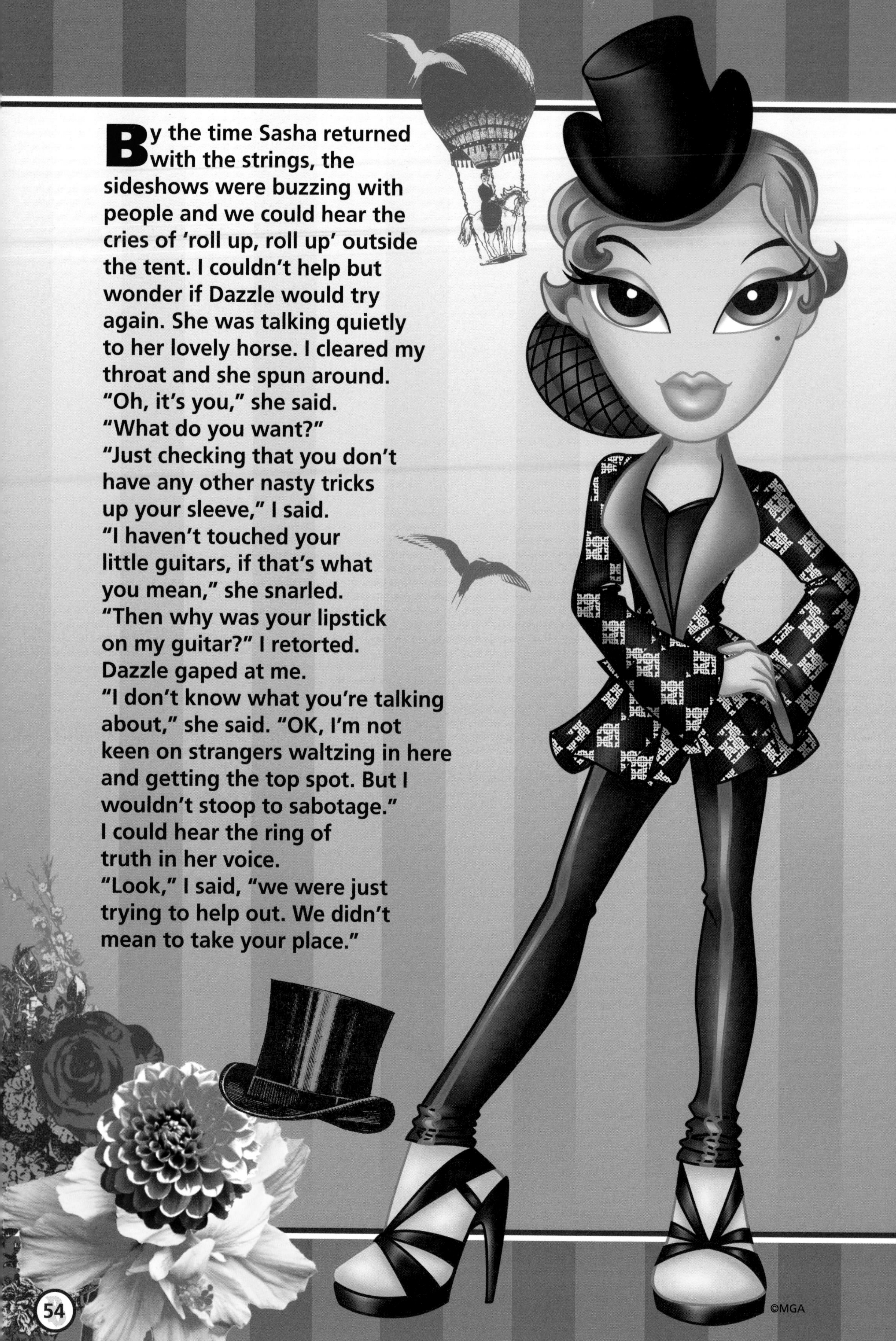

By the time Sasha returned with the strings, the sideshows were buzzing with people and we could hear the cries of 'roll up, roll up' outside the tent. I couldn't help but wonder if Dazzle would try again. She was talking quietly to her lovely horse. I cleared my throat and she spun around.

"Oh, it's you," she said. "What do you want?"

"Just checking that you don't have any other nasty tricks up your sleeve," I said.

"I haven't touched your little guitars, if that's what you mean," she snarled.

"Then why was your lipstick on my guitar?" I retorted.

Dazzle gaped at me.

"I don't know what you're talking about," she said. "OK, I'm not keen on strangers waltzing in here and getting the top spot. But I wouldn't stoop to sabotage."

I could hear the ring of truth in her voice.

"Look," I said, "we were just trying to help out. We didn't mean to take your place."

Dazzle stared at me for a moment and then let out a sigh.

"You're right," she said. "I'm sorry. I just so wanted everyone to see all the amazing things that Jet can do."

"He's a wonderful horse," I said, stroking his soft muzzle.

Dazzle gave a beaming smile and it changed her whole face. She suddenly looked younger . . . and nicer.

"I'm sorry for suspecting you," I said. "It must be someone else who wears red lipstick."

"But no one else *does,*" said Dazzle.

"This just gets weirder and weirder!" I said.

I walked slowly back towards my friends. The tent was buzzing with the chatter of the performers. I saw Jax stuffing some fake flowers into his top hat, a clownish scarlet smile painted on his white face.

The culprit had to be someone who was part of the circus. But why smear lipstick on the guitar? I stopped in my tracks. Of course! Someone wanted us to think that *Dazzle* had cut the guitar strings.

"Angel, you look as if you've seen a ghost!" said Yasmin.

I hardly heard her. Pieces of the jigsaw were coming together in my head. I knew who had sabotaged us! Of course I did!

"I know who did it!" I cried.
"What?" said the Ringmaster. "Who? Quick, Cloe – the show is about the start!"
"It was Jax!" I declared, pointing at the grinning clown.
He looked at me, and despite his painted smile, his eyes were cold.
"What are you talking about?" he said in a soft, dangerous voice.
"You made us suspect Dazzle in the first place," I said. "You, Magnifico and Dazzle offered to open the show when the Impossibles fell ill. Magnifico wouldn't have given himself food poisoning, so we know it wasn't him. That means it was either you or Dazzle."
"It was Dazzle!" declared the clown. "She even left traces of her lipstick on the guitar!"
"No," I said, "it wasn't lipstick. It was *face* paint. Dazzle's red lipstick is glossy, but the red on the guitar was matte. And if there's one thing I know about, it's makeup!"
"You interfering little –" began Jax.
"That's enough!" roared the Ringmaster. "Jax, you're not going to be performing here any more, and the police will want a word with you!"

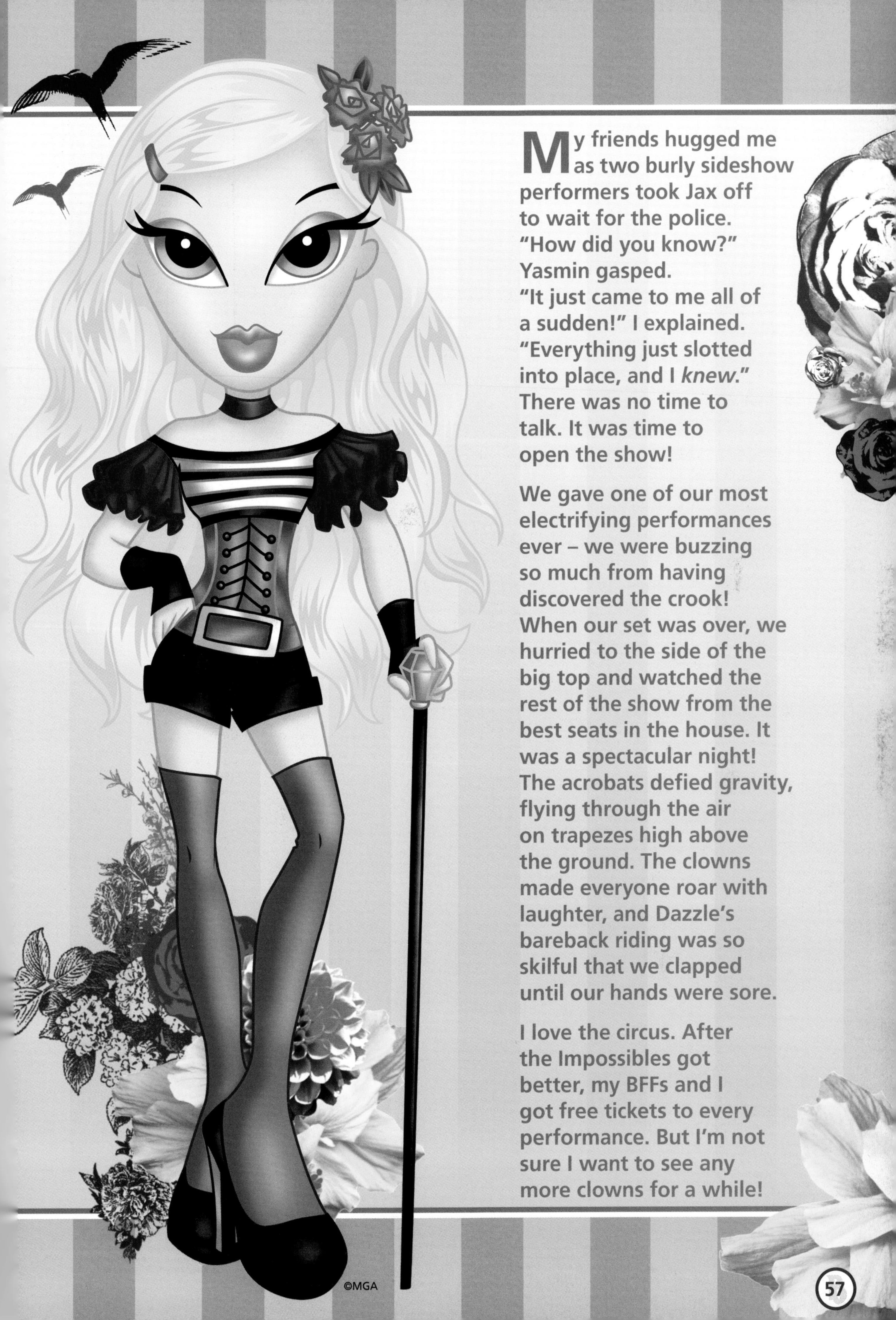

My friends hugged me as two burly sideshow performers took Jax off to wait for the police.

"How did you know?" Yasmin gasped.

"It just came to me all of a sudden!" I explained. "Everything just slotted into place, and I *knew*."

There was no time to talk. It was time to open the show!

We gave one of our most electrifying performances ever – we were buzzing so much from having discovered the crook! When our set was over, we hurried to the side of the big top and watched the rest of the show from the best seats in the house. It was a spectacular night! The acrobats defied gravity, flying through the air on trapezes high above the ground. The clowns made everyone roar with laughter, and Dazzle's bareback riding was so skilful that we clapped until our hands were sore.

I love the circus. After the Impossibles got better, my BFFs and I got free tickets to every performance. But I'm not sure I want to see any more clowns for a while!

CAPTURING KOOL KAT

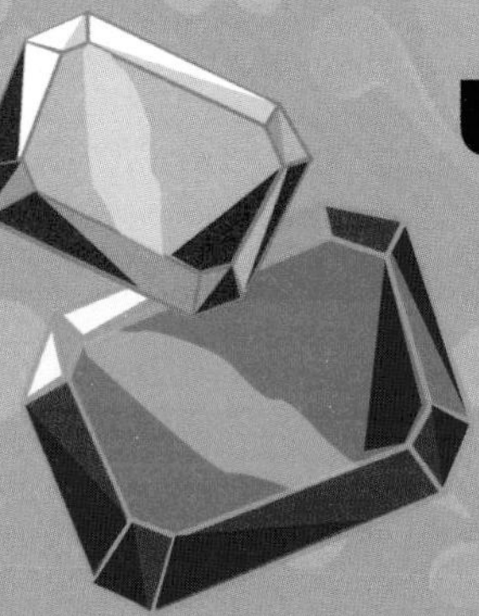

Use this grid drawing to create a perfect portrait of our fave fashion diva.

HOW TO WALK LIKE A MODEL

Whether you're putting on a fashion show or just want to show off a brand-new outfit, you and your BFFs can have great fun learning to walk like supermodels!

Your shoes are really important. Make sure that they are comfortable and that the heels are right for you. You won't look very mode-like if you're wobbling on heels that are too high!

Think about your posture. Keep your shoulders back and push your pelvis slightly forward, almost as if you are leaning back a little. You should never look hunched over.

Instead of putting your heel down first when you walk, put the ball of your foot down first, and keep your weight there.

When you walk, place one foot directly in front of the other. Your footprints should make a single line. This will give your body a beautiful, model-like swing.

Try to achieve a nice long stride by lifting each foot a good way off the ground with a bend in the knee. Don't make your strides *too* long, though, as this will make you look gangly.

Look straight forward, mirroring the vibe of the clothes you're wearing with the expression on your face. Keep your chin up and your head still.

When you make your turn at the end, your head should be the last part of your body to move.

Watch supermodels on TV. Think about that ones you noticed the most. What made them look so special?

If you stumble or fall over, don't run off in a flurry of embarrassment. Smile and keep going as if it never happened.

CREATE A FASHION DATABASE

If you have a computer and a digital camera, you can create your very own fashion database!

1. Take a picture of every item in your wardrobe. That includes accessories such as scarves, shoes, tights and hats!

2. Save the photos on to your computer.

3. Name each photo to remind you what each item of clothing is. Make sure you include the style and colour of the item in the name, plus any other distinguishing information. Work out your own naming code. For example, a picture of a red retro skirt could be called '80s red long skirt.jpg'.

4. Create folders for each type of clothing you own. For example:

Accessories

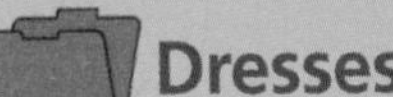
Dresses

Jumpers

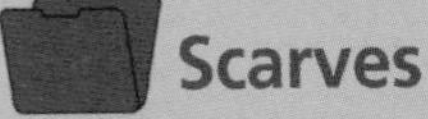
Scarves

Shoes

Shorts

Skirts

Trousers

T-shirts

5. Now you need to create folders *inside* your folders. These subfolders will be for the different types of that item. For example, in the dresses category, you might want to create subfolders for day dresses, evening dresses. Each of those folders can be given folders, for example:

- Dresses
  - Day Dresses
    - Winter Dresses
      - Long Dresses
      - Short Dresses
    - Summer Dresses
      - Long Dresses
      - Short Dresses
  - Evening Dresses
    - Winter Dresses
      - Long Dresses
      - Short Dresses
    - Summer Dresses
      - Long Dresses
      - Short Dresses

6. Sort all your photographs into the correct folders. Some items of clothing might fit into more than one folder. When that happens, just make a copy of the photo and save it in both places.

7. Now you have created your database, and you can use this to dream up stylin' new combinations and fabulous fashion statements! Play around with your images on your desktop until you have chosen every piece of your outfit. Then just pick the items out of your wardrobe!

8. Create a folder called Favourite Outfits. Whenever you create a fashion-forward new look, save it here in a subfolder. Name the folder something that will remind you what the outfit is like.

PUZZLE PAGE

		7				1		4
				8			9	
4						7	3	
		4	3				2	
6		2						9
	5					8		
9			2	4				
		8		7				
					6	5		1

START TIME:..

FINISH TIME:..

	9	3	4		6			
8		6	9			3		
	7							
			1	9		6		
		8					7	2
			5				1	
6							5	4
	8	1	7			9		6

START TIME:..

FINISH TIME:..

Sudoku is a great way to exercise your brain and keep it as sharp as your fashion sense! Challenge yourself with these four puzzles. Time how long each puzzle takes you and see if you can improve your time!

				1		5	6	
					3			4
	2		8	6		3	1	
						4		6
	9						2	7
1					4			
7		8				6		
				8	1			
6						9		

START TIME:...

FINISH TIME:...

9		1		2	4			6
	3	5	8				9	
				7			3	
6			9				2	
		9	3				6	8
	8			9		1		
3		7						

START TIME:...

FINISH TIME:...

JADE'S FASHION TIPS AND COLOUR TRENDS

I keep my eye on all the latest collections and fashion shows, and I hear plenty of secrets on the fashion grapevine. Here are my exclusive tips for the coming season!

CLOTHES

Floral prints are going to be big news over the next season, with floaty tea dresses and delicious-looking camisoles. Dresses, blouses and skirts will have a romantic feel with ruffled trims and soft frills. You can give girlyness a rock edge by accessorising with leather belts, ankle boots and studded bags.

Mini dresses, hot pants and playsuits are going to be the cutting edge of fashion, especially when worn with ankle boots.

Dresses are still hot news in the fashion stakes. They can be worn on any occasion and in any weather. They look fabulous with bare legs or with tights and boots.

A hooded jacket is a must-have for this season! It will give any look a lil' rock edge – and it will keep you warm!

Pick out a stylin' wide belt – it will help you to define a strong silhouette, and the right belt can be the final accessory that completes a fabulous outfit.

For an instant fashion fix, create some new outfits around blouses. Whether they're floaty and plain, floral, striped or checked, they look awesome with jeans or casual trousers.

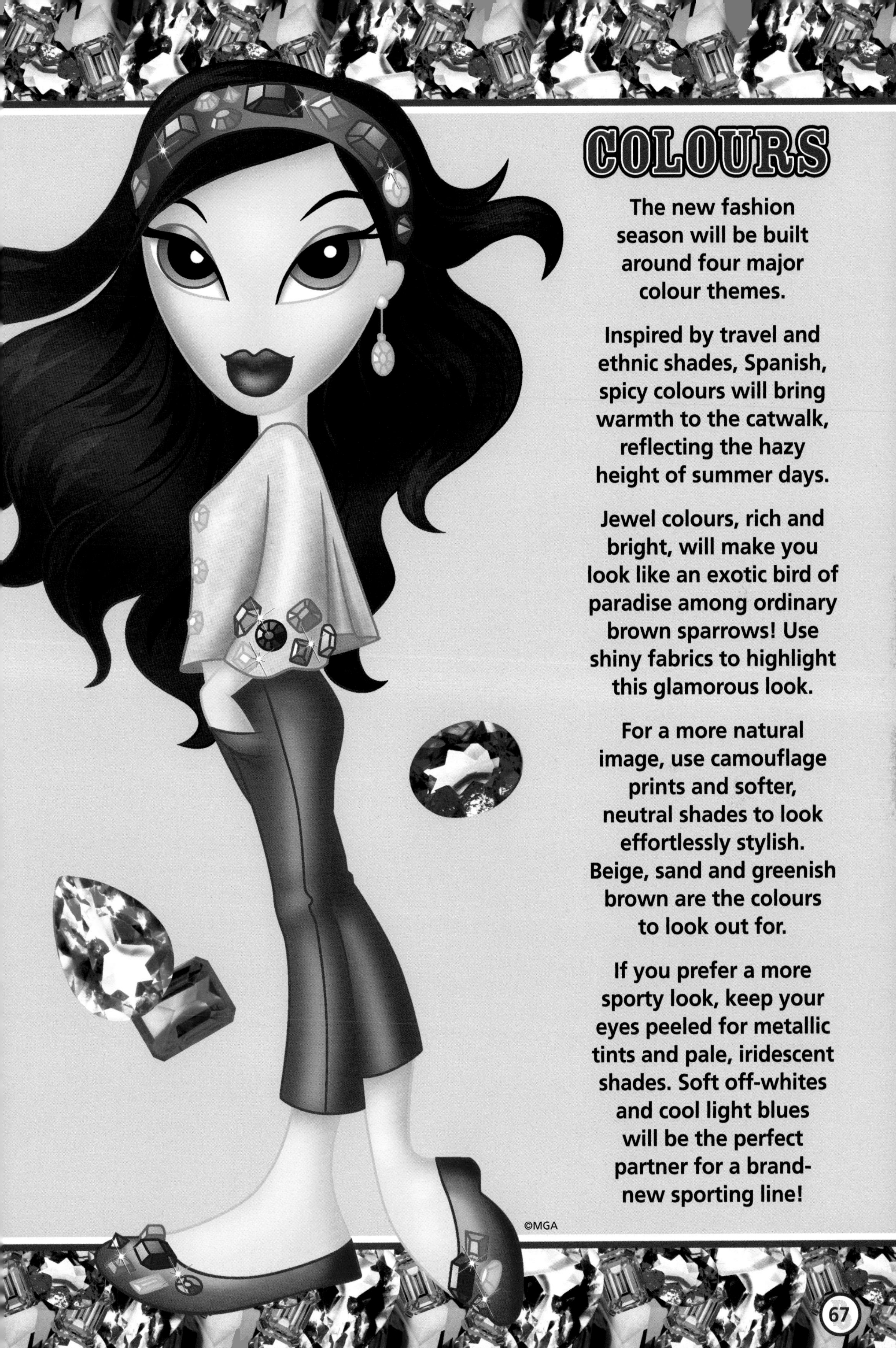

COLOURS

The new fashion season will be built around four major colour themes.

Inspired by travel and ethnic shades, Spanish, spicy colours will bring warmth to the catwalk, reflecting the hazy height of summer days.

Jewel colours, rich and bright, will make you look like an exotic bird of paradise among ordinary brown sparrows! Use shiny fabrics to highlight this glamorous look.

For a more natural image, use camouflage prints and softer, neutral shades to look effortlessly stylish. Beige, sand and greenish brown are the colours to look out for.

If you prefer a more sporty look, keep your eyes peeled for metallic tints and pale, iridescent shades. Soft off-whites and cool light blues will be the perfect partner for a brand-new sporting line!

JADE AND THE FASHION MUZE

I put down my magazine and sighed. Sasha looked up at me in surprise. We were all sitting in her garden, soaking up the first sun of the summer and reading.

"What's wrong, Kool Kat?" she enquired.

"I was just reading about all the It girls in New York and how much fun they have there in the summer," I said.

"They couldn't possibly have as much fun as we do," said Cloe. "*They* don't get to spend every gorgeous day on the beach!"

"Maybe not," I said. "But they get to hang out at the coolest parties, meet the hippest fashion designers and shop in the hottest boutiques."

I sighed again. My BFFs are great, but sometimes they don't get quite as enthusiastic about the latest fashions as I do. It can be kind of lonely always being the first to try out a new style!

"I'd rather be in Stilesville," said Yasmin. "Those celebrities are always doing silly things and having stupid arguments with each other."

"Even the top fashion designers would rather be in Stilesville," Sasha added, tossing her magazine over to me. "There's an article in there about Hannah Brox. She's in Stilesville."

"What?" I cried, grabbing the magazine.

Hannah Brox was the name on everyone's lips – the hottest new label in the world of fashion. Her clothes were super-exclusive and celebrities were falling over themselves to get her to design something for them.

"She's the one who's got a new best friend every week isn't she?" said Cloe with a laugh.

I chose to ignore her. My friends had never understood how talented Hannah was. The article said that Hannah was in town to visit the new boutique she was opening, and to get a feel for fashion outside New York. I devoured every word of the article.

"What shall we do tomorrow?" said Yasmin, stretching sleepily in the sun.

"Beach!" chorused Cloe and Sasha.

I said nothing, but I wasn't planning to join them at the beach. I had some shopping to do.

Next day I raced to the mall to check out Hannah Brox's new boutique. It was fabulous – her clothes were edgy and unique, with unusual combinations of colour and texture that were totally inspiring. As I walked around the mall afterwards, it was as if I was looking with new eyes. I seemed to see colours and shapes in a brand-new way. I picked out some new separates, seeing the outfits I would put together in my mind's eye.

That afternoon I walked over to Cloe's house in my new outfit. I had paired purple capri trousers with a vest top and a swing jacket, and I had decorated the sleeves with jewels to match my shoes and simple hairband. When I was halfway to Cloe's house, I heard a cry and a car screeched to a halt next to me. Then a woman jumped out and I gasped. It was Hannah Brox!

"My muse!" she cried, grabbing me by the shoulders. "Oh, your style is totally fresh! It's so in tune with my own direction! I love it!"

"Thanks," I said, blushing furiously.

"Just looking at you gives me tons of ideas for new outfits!" she continued. "You're an inspiration – I must take you with me to New York!"

I had heard that Hannah Brox was eccentric, but this was crazy!

"What?" I began.

Hannah held up her hand and stopped me.

"No arguments!" she said. "I will show you the true wonders of the fashion world – you will be my muse! My protégée!"

". . . so she wants me to leave for New York with her tonight," I finished telling the others later that afternoon. Isn't it amazing!"

"Amazing," said Yasmin in a flat sort of voice.

"She sounds a bit mad to me," Cloe murmured.

"Of course, you're not going," said Sasha.

"Of course I *am*!" I said, feeling my temper flare suddenly. "Why shouldn't I? You're all just jealous!"

"Kool Kat!" gasped Yasmin, looking horrified.

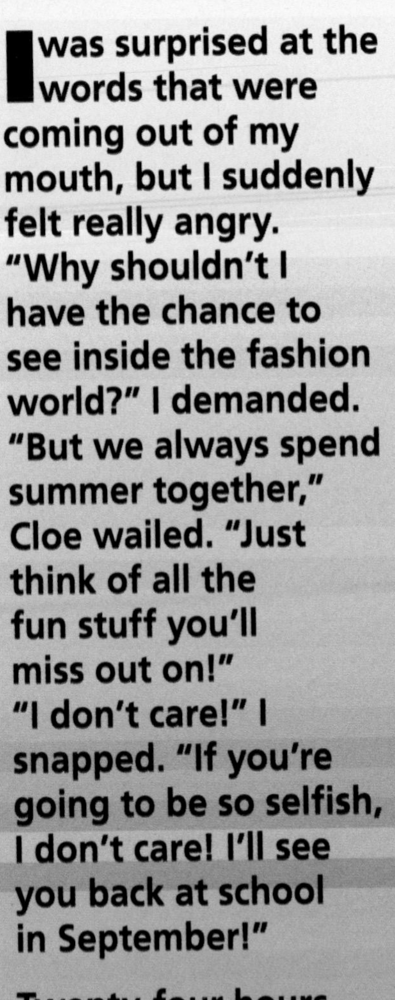

I was surprised at the words that were coming out of my mouth, but I suddenly felt really angry. "Why shouldn't I have the chance to see inside the fashion world?" I demanded.

"But we always spend summer together," Cloe wailed. "Just think of all the fun stuff you'll miss out on!"

"I don't care!" I snapped. "If you're going to be so selfish, I don't care! I'll see you back at school in September!"

Twenty-four hours later, I was sitting in my hotel room in New York, wishing that I had made up with my friends before I left Stilesville. But Sasha had flared up and I had stormed out.

I stuck my chin in the air. They seemed to think that Hannah Brox would drop me as soon as she got bored of me, but I knew she wasn't like that. I'd show them!

"Jade, darling!" cried Hannah when I arrived at her studio the next morning. She rushed over and enveloped me in a huge hug.

"Everyone, I want to introduce Jade!" she cried, pushing me forward.

The studio seemed to be filled with stunning models, super-cool designers and bustling assistants. Large tables were covered in fabulous materials and the air was heavy with expensive perfume.

Several women turned and looked at me. I recognised them from my magazines – some of the well-known It girls who were always being photographed and interviewed.

"So you're the latest muse, are you?" drawled one of them, a curly-haired blonde girl called Poppy.

"She's already given me some electrifying ideas!" declared Hannah. "Jade darling, stay here with the girls while I go and sketch my designs before I lose them."

She whisked off into another room and I was left with Poppy and another girl who was checking her makeup in a hand mirror. She had shiny auburn hair and her name was Flora.

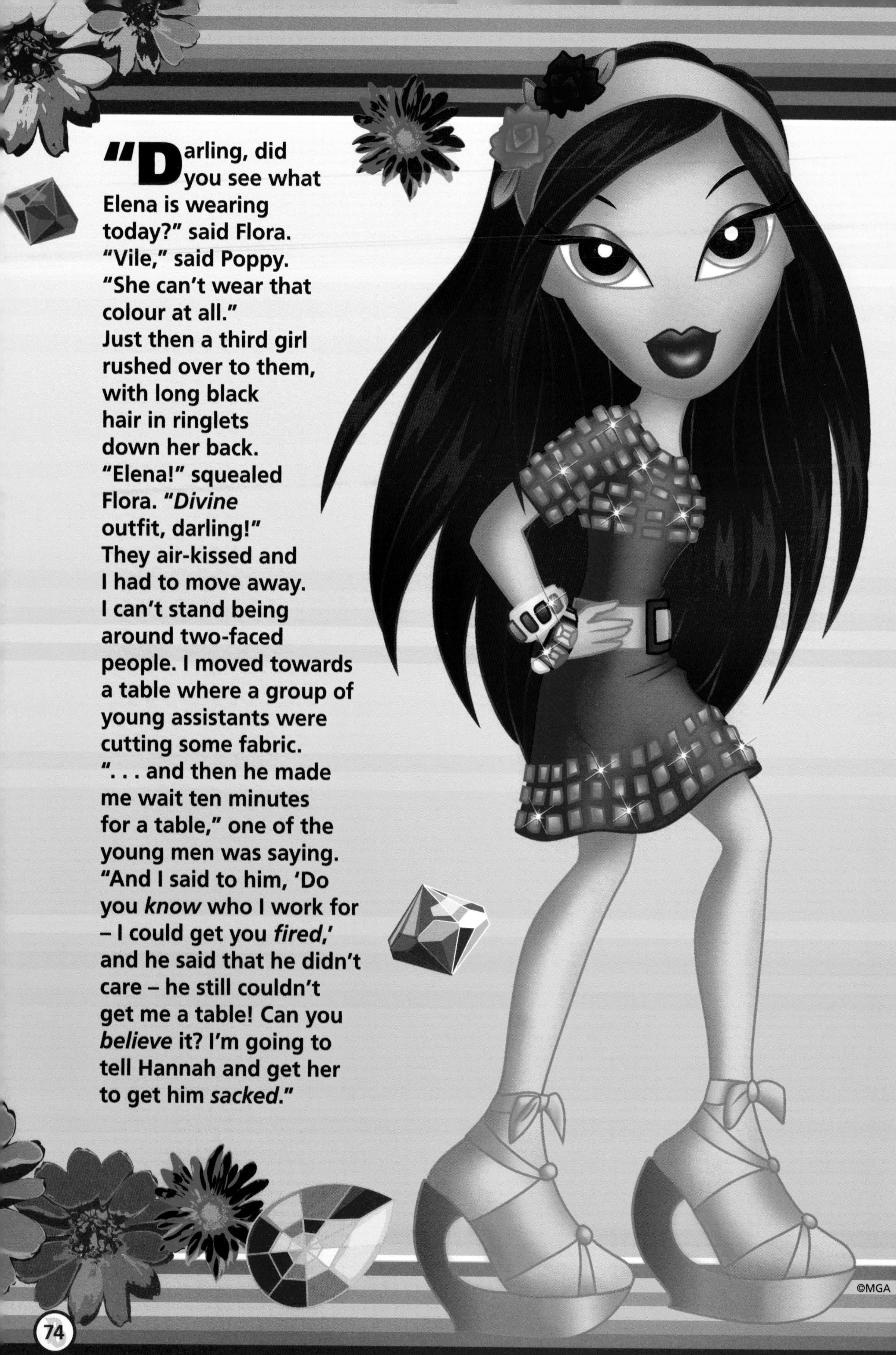

"Darling, did you see what Elena is wearing today?" said Flora.
"Vile," said Poppy. "She can't wear that colour at all."
Just then a third girl rushed over to them, with long black hair in ringlets down her back.
"Elena!" squealed Flora. "*Divine* outfit, darling!"
They air-kissed and I had to move away. I can't stand being around two-faced people. I moved towards a table where a group of young assistants were cutting some fabric.
". . . and then he made me wait ten minutes for a table," one of the young men was saying. "And I said to him, 'Do you *know* who I work for – I could get you *fired*,' and he said that he didn't care – he still couldn't get me a table! Can you *believe* it? I'm going to tell Hannah and get her to get him *sacked*."

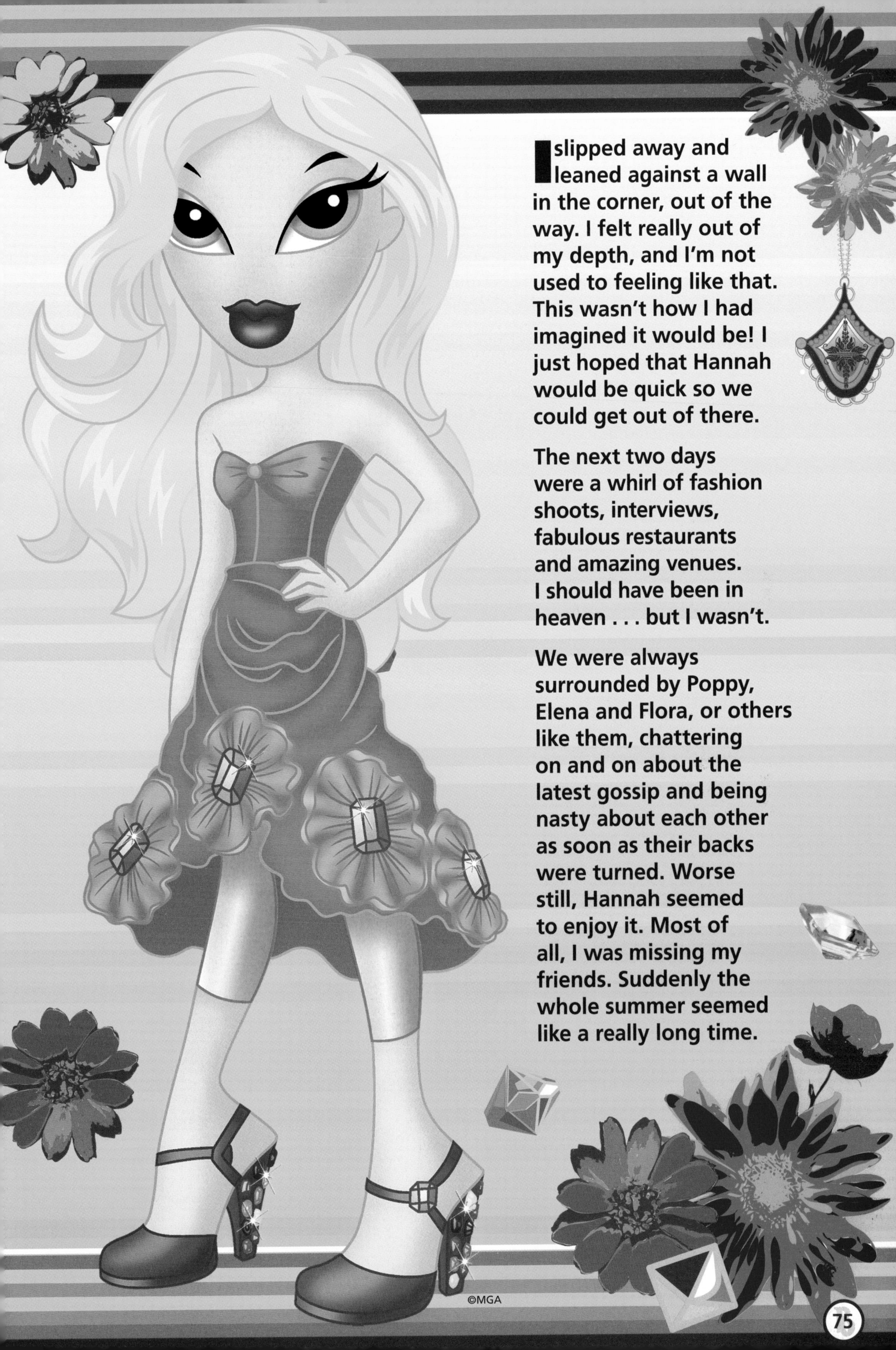

I slipped away and leaned against a wall in the corner, out of the way. I felt really out of my depth, and I'm not used to feeling like that. This wasn't how I had imagined it would be! I just hoped that Hannah would be quick so we could get out of there.

The next two days were a whirl of fashion shoots, interviews, fabulous restaurants and amazing venues. I should have been in heaven . . . but I wasn't.

We were always surrounded by Poppy, Elena and Flora, or others like them, chattering on and on about the latest gossip and being nasty about each other as soon as their backs were turned. Worse still, Hannah seemed to enjoy it. Most of all, I was missing my friends. Suddenly the whole summer seemed like a really long time.

I had hoped that I would be able to learn from Hannah, but when she actually did anything creative, she went into her private office and shut the door. I saw a few of her sketches and they were all of me and what I was wearing. I guessed she must be recording my outfits for inspiration.

On the third day, we were sitting around a large, circular table in one of New York's most exclusive restaurants. I was keeping my head down and trying not to listen to Poppy's stream of nasty gossip. "Her hair looked a real mess," Poppy was saying. "And her *outfit*!" Elena added. "I mean, it wasn't even *designer*!" Everyone laughed, including Hannah, and suddenly I saw red. I had been listening to this kind of thing for days, and I had had enough!

"You don't know anything about fashion!" I exploded, flinging down my knife and fork. "You think it's all about money and where you're seen and who's 'in' and who's 'out'! Fashion's about beauty and creativity, and you don't need money for that!"

"It certainly helps, though!" Hannah said with a sneering laugh.

With that, it was as if a blindfold was taken off my eyes and I saw Hannah for what she really was.

"You're just as bad as the rest of them!" I said. "Fashion shouldn't be about being nasty to people! I thought you were a good designer, but you use other people's talent. I'm not your muse – you're just stealing my ideas!"

"Well, if that's how you feel, you can just run home to Stilesville," snapped Hannah, looking embarrassed.

"I will," I said, smoothly. "And I'll tell everyone what you're really like."

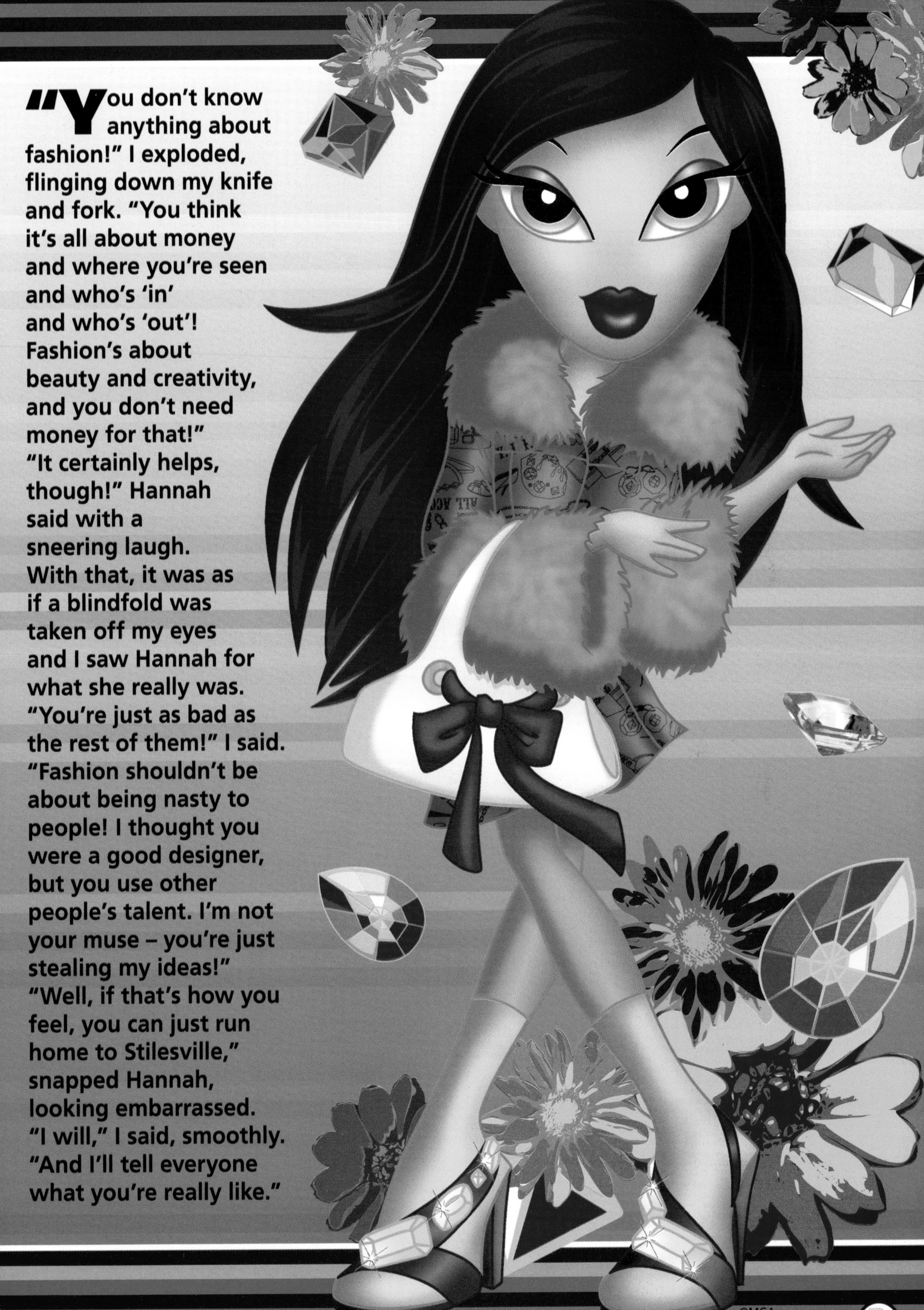

I stood up, pushed back my chair and walked out. Everyone in the restaurant had heard what I said and I knew that it would be all over the celebrity magazines. But I didn't feel satisfied – I just felt silly.

I raced back to my hotel, determined not to cry. I opened my room door . . . and gaped as my BFFs rushed towards me! "What are you guys doing here?" I cried as we all shared a massive hug. "You didn't think we were going to let you stay here all summer?" Sasha demanded. "We thought you might be sick of the glamorous world of fashion by now!" Yasmin said with a twinkle in her eyes. "We can't do without you, Kool Kat," said Cloe, slipping her arm around my waist. "You guys," I said. "You have no idea how glad I am to see you!"

I told them all about Hannah and her fake world. As I was talking, Sasha pulled out my suitcase and started to pack.

"Hang on," said Cloe. "Let's not rush this."

"What are you saying, Angel?" I asked. "I've made up my mind – I'm going back to Stilesville with you!"

"Of course," said Cloe. "But we are in New York. And it's not the world of fashion you dislike – it's the world of Hannah Brox."

"And there *are* some fabulous shopping venues in this city," I added, catching on to Cloe's meaning.

"We have some serious shopping to do!" Yasmin declared.

We all smiled at each other.

"I'm sorry I was so silly," I said. "I just got dazzled."

"It's all forgotten," said Sasha. "Besides, we can't do without you, girl. You're *our* fashion muse!"

Music Preferences

Here's your chance to make a record of all the things you love and hate in the music scene! Check back to your answers in twelve months' time and see if you still think the same. Hey – it's also great practice for when you're a music star and answering fans' questions in magazines!

Today's date:

....

1. What is your fave music style?

....

2. What kind of music do you predict will be popular in five years' time?

....

3. List your five fave female singers.

....

....

....

....

....

4. Write out the chorus of your fave song.

....

....

....

5. If you were in a musical, which one would you choose and why?

....

6. What was the last concert you went to?

....

7. Who are your top five bands?

....

....

....

....

....

8. Which song would you like to dance to with your crush?

....

9. Make a list of your top five male singers.

....

....

....

....

....

10. Which song do you like to dance to with your BFFs?

....

11. Name your five top musicians.

....

....

....

....

....

12. Which music star would you most like to sing with?

....

13. Which five songs best describe your friendship with your BFFs?

....

....

....

....

....

14. What is the last song you listened to on your MP3 player or CD player?

....

15. Make a list of five songs you would like to sing to your crush.

....

....

....

....

....

16. Who would you most like to see in concert next?

....

17. What did you last sing in the shower?

....

wordsearch

Search through this grid for the ten words that are hidden there. They are all items of clothing. As you find each one, write it down in the spaces below

R	J	S	R	S	A	L	I	B	R	H	N	F	D
E	L	T	R	O	U	S	E	R	S	M	S	A	R
P	A	R	X	D	C	F	Q	J	O	I	K	O	H
M	G	O	I	B	U	T	L	L	Y	H	E	C	D
U	W	H	S	U	L	R	B	O	O	E	A	M	X
J	D	S	B	W	I	O	D	A	C	M	Z	S	N
U	L	M	C	D	O	Y	U	L	I	G	K	U	R
B	T	I	D	T	S	K	H	S	L	U	W	B	G
A	R	J	S	J	X	E	O	H	E	A	T	E	Q
S	I	T	Q	S	W	L	G	K	S	D	A	I	W
I	K	C	A	R	E	H	M	Z	U	L	O	M	B
D	S	X	U	G	K	I	D	R	A	X	C	A	E
Q	J	T	W	S	S	E	R	D	T	B	U	J	L
B	D	H	L	R	I	K	T	S	F	U	O	R	T

1. ....
2. ....
3. ....
4. ....
5. ....
6. ....
7. ....
8. ....
9. ....
10. ....

accessories matter!

Design some rockin' accessories to complete Sasha's super-stylin' image. Finish her look with some bold, bright colours.

2009 calendar

Check out our stylin' 2009 calendar! Use this space to write down all your most important dates!

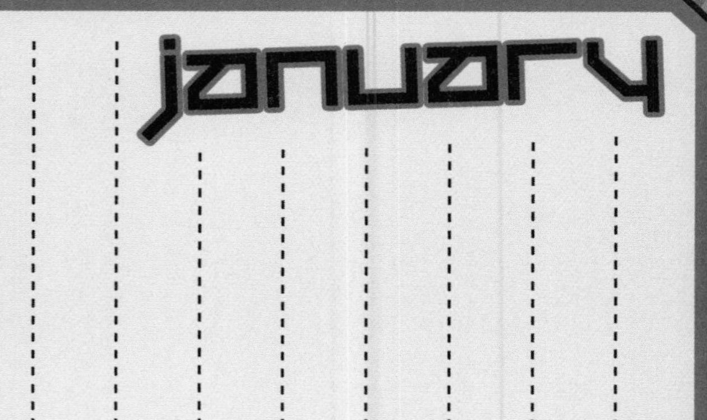

january

february

march

april

may

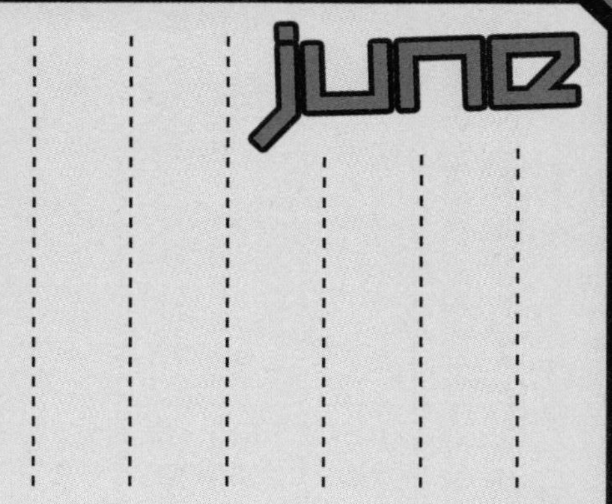

june

july
august
september
october
november
december

sasha's sports guide:

windsurfing

Windsurfing is one of my all-time fave sports! It's a huge adrenaline rush and a great way to meet new friends. Nothing beats the excitement of skimming across the foaming waves at 30mph, feeling like you're part of the elements! (Nothing except putting on a fantastic DJ performance, of course . . .) Windsurfing can reduce your stress levels and it's a super-friendly sport – it doesn't matter how inexperienced you are, you'll be welcomed right in!

Don't worry – you don't have to be incredibly strong to be good at windsurfing. You can get amazingly light boards, and sails are available in many shapes and sizes.

equipment

Rig – Sail, mast, mast-foot, uphaul rope and boom. You'll find out more about what all these things are when you start training.

Board – A widestyle board is perfect for a beginner. Remember, width and volume are more important than length. Choose a board by using this simple formula:

(Weight of rig, board and clothing in kg) + (your weight in kg x 2) = volume of board in litres.

Clothing – You will need a wetsuit. Choose a stylin' one-piece suit made with a 'blind stitch'. This is a stitch that doesn't let water through. The suit should not be too tight or too loose. And of course, it should be fashion forward!

Buoyancy Aid – This gives you extra ability to float. It will help you to feel more confident and to be safer.

Training – Find a training centre that's listed with the Royal Yachting Association. A beginners' course will teach you all the windsurfing basics.

Boots and Gloves – Just like on dry land, these will protect you in cold weather!

If you are heading towards another windsurfer, you need to know who has the right of way. The simple rule is that if your right hand is nearest the mast on the boom, you have right of way.

You should give way to any vessel or person that cannot move as easily or quickly as you can, such as swimmers or rowers.

getting started

You'll learn how to start windsurfing at a training centre, but these are some of the things you'll be taught!

1. Carry the board to the water first, and then the sail.

2. Check out the wind direction. As long as the wind is right, attach the sail and board together.

3. When you have walked past knee-deep water, push the board down into a vertical position.

4. Stand so that the wind is behind you and the rig. You should stand on the side of the board that is opposite to the rig.

5. Get up on to the board and on to your knees. Put your hands on either side of the mast.

6. Stand up and start to pull up the sail. Bend down and reach for the uphaul rope. Bend your knees but don't bend your back.

7. Slowly straighten your legs and lean back.

8. Pull the sail a little way out of the water. Pull on the rope hand over hand until you reach the mast.

9. Use both hands to grab the mast just below the boom.

10. Choose a point to aim for on the water. This point should be ahead of you and at right angles to the direction of the wind.

11. Let go of the mast with your back hand. Move your back foot towards the back of the board. Point your front foot towards the front of the board, with your toes almost in line with the mast.

12. Your body should face the direction in which you want to go.

13. Pull the rig at right angles to the board, grabbing the boom with your back hand. Now pull the rig in so that the sail fills with wind. Your weight should be on your back foot.

14. Put your front hand on to the boom. Now you are in sailing position. Try to sail towards your aiming point at right angles to the wind.

15. Keep your head up and look where you are going.

16. Your arms should be slightly bent, your back straight and your bottom tucked in. Keep your front leg straight and your back leg bent. Your feet should be kept shoulder width apart.

What's your perfect seaside activity?

Answer these questions and find out what would be the best seaside sport for you to try.

1 Which of these statements comes closest to describing you?

a. I am sporty and fairly impatient. ☐
b. I am sporty and quite patient. ☐
c. I am not usually very keen on sport. ☐

2 What's your ideal holiday?

a. Activities-based holiday. ☐
b. Beach holiday on the Australian coast. ☐
c. British seaside in the sun. ☐

3 Which type of sport do you prefer?

a. Solo sports like skiing. ☐
b. Team sports like athletics. ☐
c. I really, *really* don't like sport! ☐

4 When do you like the sea best?

a. When it's grey-green and slightly stormy. ☐
b. When it's blue and the waves are huge. ☐
c. When it's warm enough to swim in. ☐

5 How do you feel about the weather?

a. I love to go walking in storms. ☐
b. I like windy days – they're exhilarating. ☐
c. I like warm, sunny days. ☐

6 When you are sunbathing, how do you feel?

a. Irritable – you hate to lie still for too long. ☐

b. Chatty – you like having your mates around you. ☐

c. Content and sleepy – you just lie back and soak up the rays. ☐

7 Which of these statements is most true of you?

a. I am a risk taker. ☐

b. I am very calm. ☐

c. I like to feel safe. ☐

8 Which of these artists do you like best?

a. Scouting for Girls. ☐

b. The Beach Boys. ☐

c. Rhianna. ☐

9 What's your ideal party scene?

a. A elegant party. ☐

b. Midnight beach party. ☐

c. Nightclub. ☐

10 How do you think you would react in a dangerous situation?

a. I would try to take control of the situation. ☐

b. I would try to calm everyone down. ☐

c. I would feel scared and wait to be told what to do. ☐

Now add up how many As, Bs and Cs you have, and check out your answers below.

mostly as – You are focused, sporty and you like a challenge. You would enjoy windsurfing best.

mostly bs – You're laid back and super-calm, but you're wild at heart! You're a natural-born surfer girl.

mostly cs – You don't enjoy putting yourself in danger – adrenalin rushes are not your thing! You'll enjoy body boarding.

Sasha and the punk problem

"Is everything organised?" Cloe asked me for the millionth time.

"Angel, this is Bunny Boo you're talking to," said Yasmin with a laugh.

"It's always worth double checking though," I said, pulling out my list. I know they think I can be a bit obsessive about organising things, but seriously, someone's got to do it! And this charity concert was one of the biggest things I had ever planned. It had taken weeks to get everything together, and if anything went wrong I was going to freak out.

I had called in every favour I could, and twenty awesome performers were descending on Stilesville for a one-off, one-night-only concert. We were raising money for Yasmin's fave animal charity, and we had sold all the tickets. I even had a top music producer coming along – my friend Nathan Harlow. I ran my eye down the list. I had organised the venue, the refreshments, the decorations for the hall, the seating . . . everything was ready.

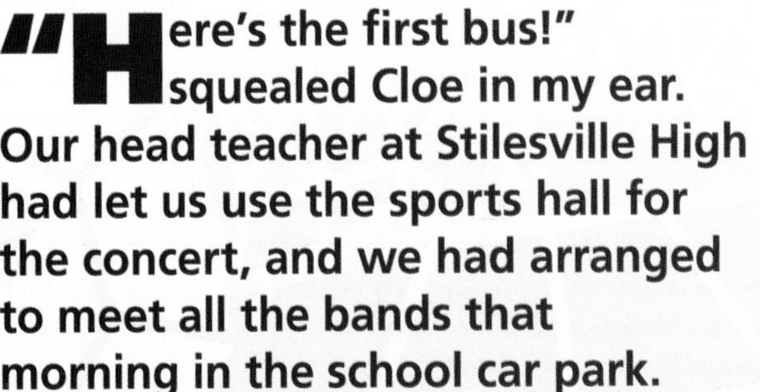

"Here's the first bus!" squealed Cloe in my ear. Our head teacher at Stilesville High had let us use the sports hall for the concert, and we had arranged to meet all the bands that morning in the school car park.

The next hour was insanely busy. I ticked off each act as they arrived. Then Cloe, Jade and Yasmin showed them to the sports hall so that they could unload their equipment. I could hardly believe it was all going so smoothly! As the last act headed towards the sports hall with Yasmin, I felt a tap on my shoulder. It was Nathan Harlow and he was grinning at me.
"Are you hoping to spot a few undiscovered talents in there?" I said, smiling back at him.
"You've got a great ear, Sasha," he said. "If you think they're worth listening to, I trust you!"
We headed towards the hall together.

Shortly, I was standing in the sports hall surrounded by awesome musical talents. I was in heaven! I cleared my throat and gave the short speech I had prepared.

"First, I'd like to thank you all for being here today," I said. "Some of you have arrived with lots of people, some are solo acts with no assistants. Some are famous and some are undiscovered. But the great thing is that you are all giving your time and talent to this great cause."

I paused while everyone cheered and clapped. When the noise died down, I continued.

"We all need to be ready by half past seven tonight," I said. "There's a lot to prepare. But first, the school canteen has offered to put on a brunch for us all, free of charge. So we'll head across there now, have something to eat and drink, and then start to set up. Is that OK with everyone?"

The cheer that went up told me it was!

In the canteen, I hardly had the chance to speak to my BFFs. We were hosting the concert, and that meant we had to say hi to everyone. We walked around the bustling café, hugging old friends and greeting new ones. There were so many people to see that at first I didn't notice that one person wasn't taking part.

A dark-haired girl was standing at the far end of the canteen, looking pale and miserable. I frowned, trying to place her. Of course, she could just be there to help one of the bands out. But I was sure that I had seen her performing. I just couldn't remember where. I couldn't even remember ticking her off on my list.

As I watched, I saw a man and woman go up to her. I recognised them as the parents of one of the acts – a fantastic punk singer I had seen months before at a local school concert. Of course, she was Ali Thorn!

The girl looked very different from the punk rocker I had seen on stage. When I had seen her she had been wearing a stylin' ripped tee and skinny jeans, and her hair had been spiked up and dyed black and red. Now her hair was brown and neatly combed flat, and she was wearing a pink dress that looked as if it belonged on a five-year old. I went over to her.

"Hi," I said. "I'm Sasha – I think we spoke on the phone?"

The girl just looked at me.

"Are you feeling a bit shy?" I asked. "It's understandable with all these famous acts here, but you just have to remember that you're one of them! Your punk act is one of the best I've ever heard!"

At this, Ali's face flushed red and she glanced at her parents.

"I'm not a punk singer," she spat out. "My act is 'songs from the musicals'."

"What?" I gasped.

Before I could say any more, her mother interrupted. "Our little Allegra's going to be the star of the show," said her mother, pinching Ali's cheek. "Allegra?" I repeated. "I thought her name was Ali. And when I saw her perform, she was a punk singer." "That was just a silly phase, wasn't it," said her father, his lips tight. "Right," I said slowly. "Well, I will have to rethink her position in the show. I'm not sure where a . . . er. . . selection from the musicals will fit in, but I'll find a place." I walked away, but not before I saw the flash of misery in Ali's eyes.

Soon it was time to start rehearsing the bands. For a while I forgot about Ali – there was so much to organise. But when I went outside to take a break, I saw her sitting on a bench. She was leaning forwards with her elbows on her knees and her hands supporting her chin.

I went and sat beside her.

"Hi . . . Allegra," I said softly.

"Don't call me that," she snapped. "Oh, just leave me alone. I wish I'd never come."

I have a bit of a temper, and normally I would have done exactly as she asked and left with a few choice words about her rudeness. But I was stopped by the memory of that flash of misery in her eyes.

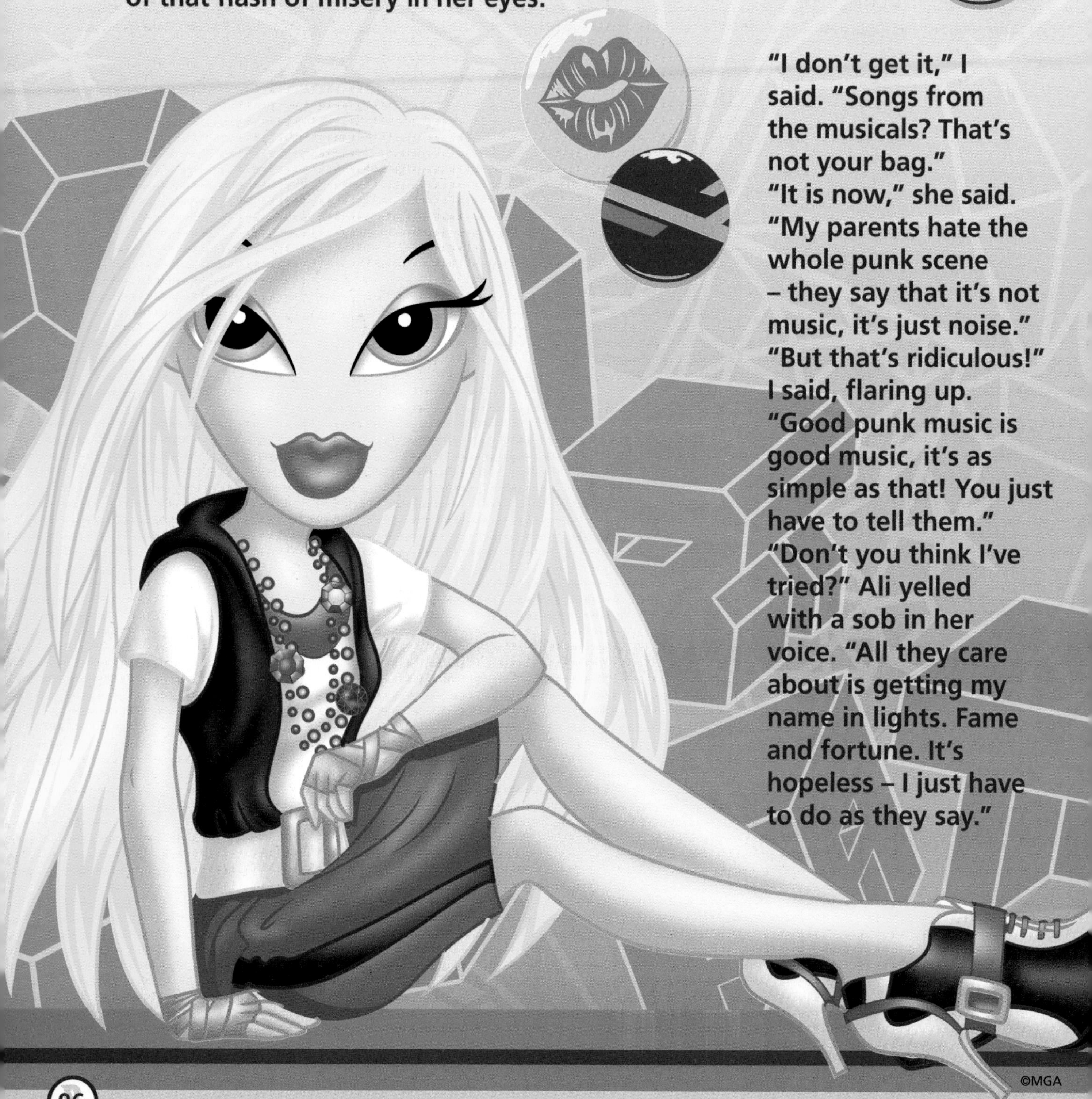

"I don't get it," I said. "Songs from the musicals? That's not your bag."

"It is now," she said. "My parents hate the whole punk scene – they say that it's not music, it's just noise."

"But that's ridiculous!" I said, flaring up. "Good punk music is good music, it's as simple as that! You just have to tell them."

"Don't you think I've tried?" Ali yelled with a sob in her voice. "All they care about is getting my name in lights. Fame and fortune. It's hopeless – I just have to do as they say."

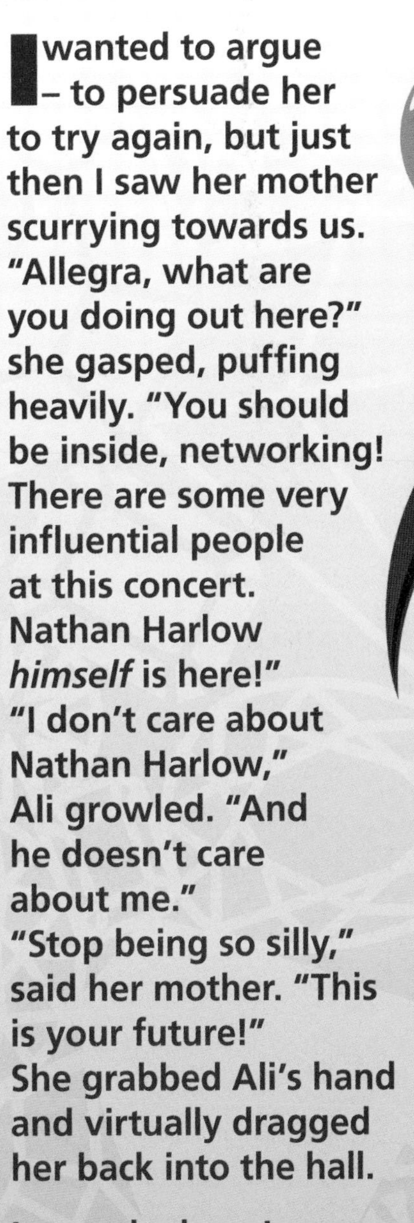

I wanted to argue – to persuade her to try again, but just then I saw her mother scurrying towards us. "Allegra, what are you doing out here?" she gasped, puffing heavily. "You should be inside, networking! There are some very influential people at this concert. Nathan Harlow *himself* is here!"
"I don't care about Nathan Harlow," Ali growled. "And he doesn't care about me."
"Stop being so silly," said her mother. "This is your future!"
She grabbed Ali's hand and virtually dragged her back into the hall.

I stayed where I was. A little idea had started to form in my mind. Mr and Mrs Thorn obviously cared more about fame than they did about music. They were snobs. A smile crept over my face. Fine, I would play up to their snobbery.

Back inside the sports hall, there was a cacophony of sound and chatter as twenty different bands tuned up, practised and discussed their numbers. Cloe and Yasmin were painting some last-minute backdrop scenes, and Jade was tucked into a corner, sketching frantically. I guessed that all the fashion styles around us had sent her imagination racing! Everyone looked happy enough, so I made a beeline for Nathan Harlow and pulled him to one side.

I told Nathan about Ali's amazing punk act and explained what I wanted him to do. "Like I said, if you think someone's got talent, I trust your judgment," said Nathan. "I just hope that her parents don't see through it." "It's not as if you're going to be saying anything that isn't true," I reminded him. "OK, Sasha, you win!" he laughed. "I wouldn't dare to stand in your way!"

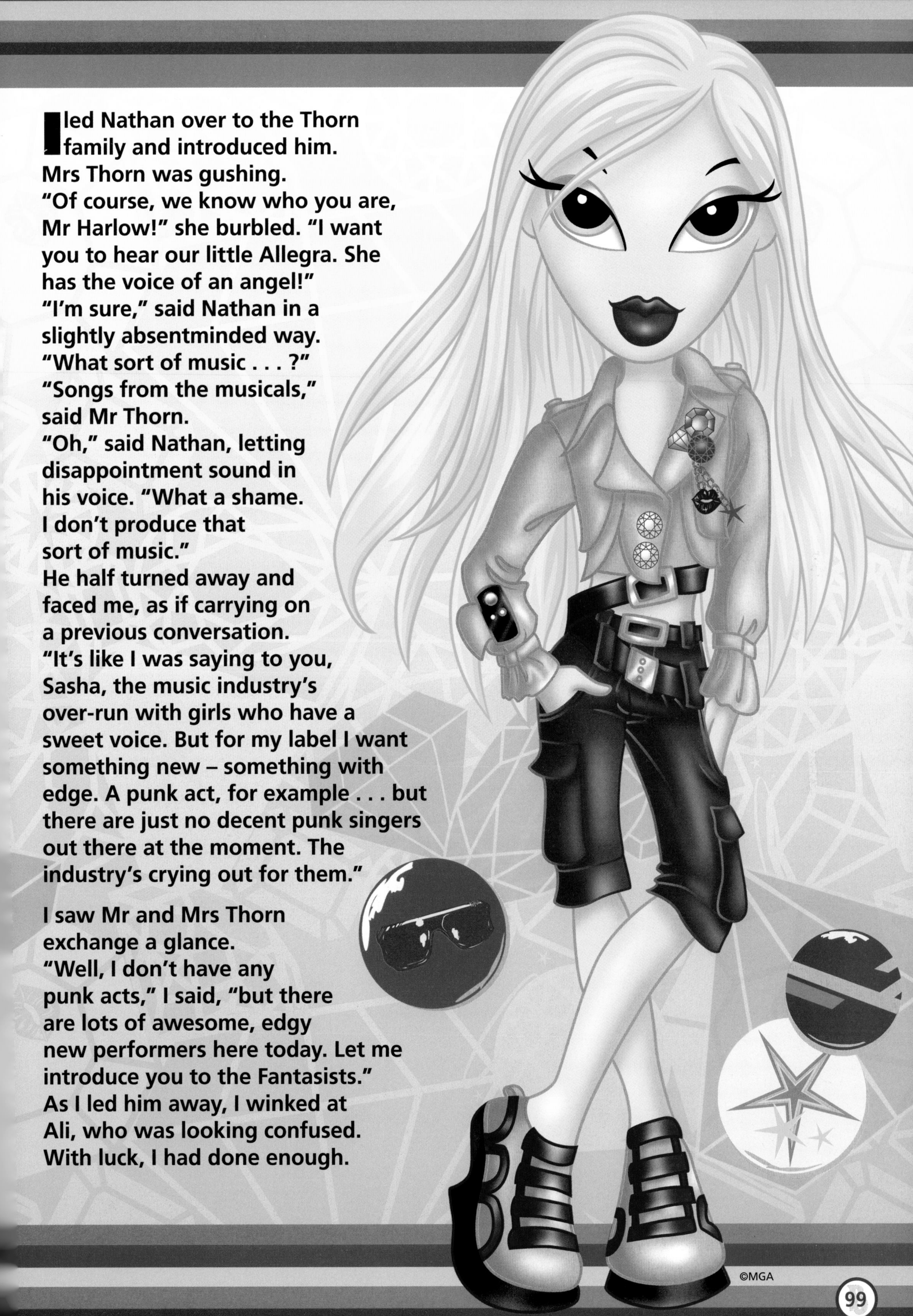

I led Nathan over to the Thorn family and introduced him. Mrs Thorn was gushing.
"Of course, we know who you are, Mr Harlow!" she burbled. "I want you to hear our little Allegra. She has the voice of an angel!"
"I'm sure," said Nathan in a slightly absentminded way. "What sort of music . . . ?"
"Songs from the musicals," said Mr Thorn.
"Oh," said Nathan, letting disappointment sound in his voice. "What a shame. I don't produce that sort of music."
He half turned away and faced me, as if carrying on a previous conversation.
"It's like I was saying to you, Sasha, the music industry's over-run with girls who have a sweet voice. But for my label I want something new – something with edge. A punk act, for example . . . but there are just no decent punk singers out there at the moment. The industry's crying out for them."

I saw Mr and Mrs Thorn exchange a glance.
"Well, I don't have any punk acts," I said, "but there are lots of awesome, edgy new performers here today. Let me introduce you to the Fantasists."
As I led him away, I winked at Ali, who was looking confused. With luck, I had done enough.

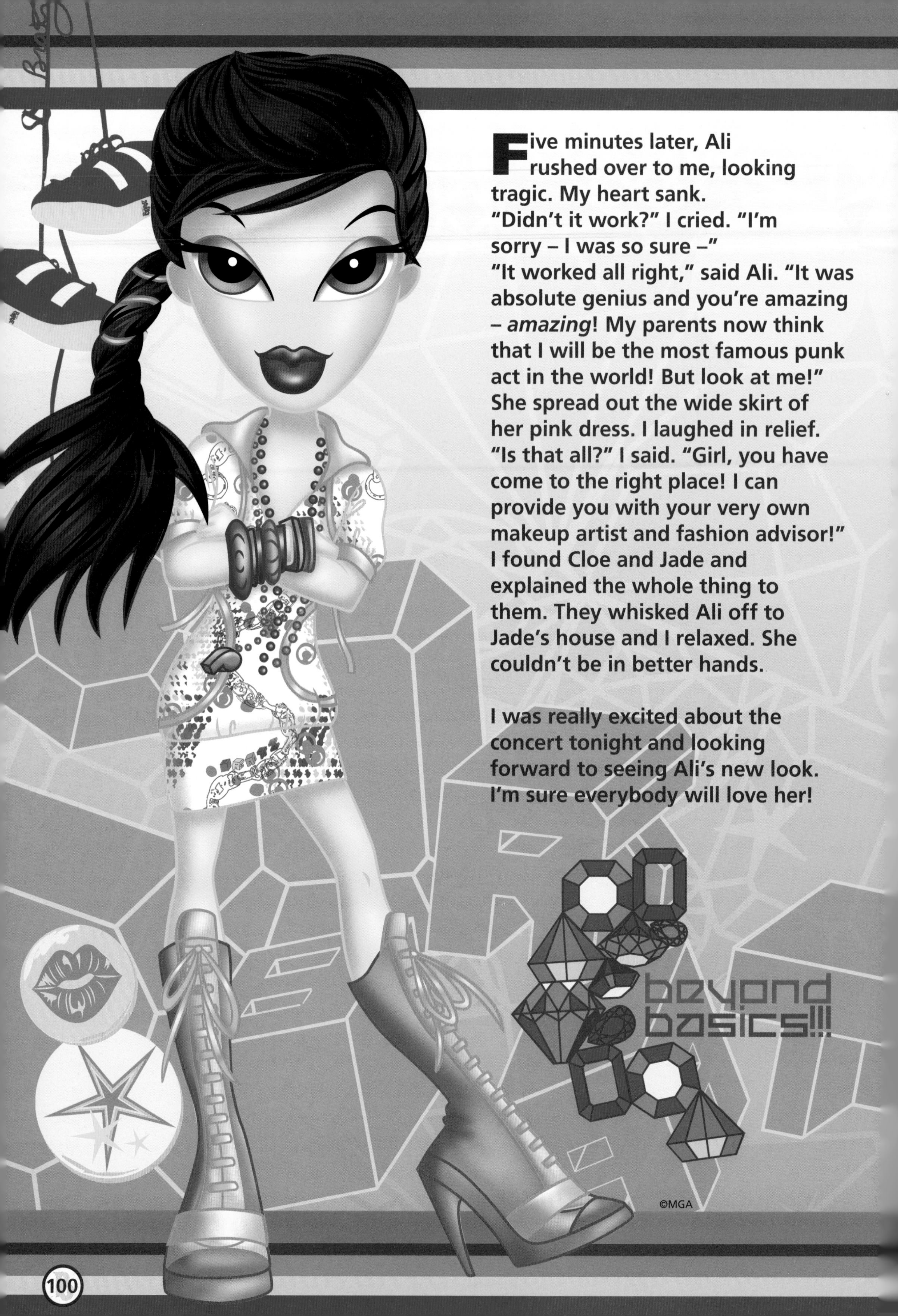

Five minutes later, Ali rushed over to me, looking tragic. My heart sank.

"Didn't it work?" I cried. "I'm sorry – I was so sure –"

"It worked all right," said Ali. "It was absolute genius and you're amazing – *amazing*! My parents now think that I will be the most famous punk act in the world! But look at me!" She spread out the wide skirt of her pink dress. I laughed in relief.

"Is that all?" I said. "Girl, you have come to the right place! I can provide you with your very own makeup artist and fashion advisor!" I found Cloe and Jade and explained the whole thing to them. They whisked Ali off to Jade's house and I relaxed. She couldn't be in better hands.

I was really excited about the concert tonight and looking forward to seeing Ali's new look. I'm sure everybody will love her!

The concert was so mind-blowingly awesome that it has gone down in Stilesville history. The highlight of the evening came when a spiky-haired girl stepped on to the stage with a borrowed guitar. Her makeup was a fusion of classic punk and modern funk, and she wore a chainlink cami top over a ripped tee and frayed denims with white lace edging. Then she started to sing, and the crowd was carried away on a pumped-up wave of perfect punk rock.

At the end of the concert, Ali rushed up and hugged me tightly. "Nathan's giving me a recording contract!" she gasped. "Mum and Dad are over the moon, and it's all thanks to you! How can I ever repay you?" "You don't have to," I replied, laughing. "Knowing that I helped you get your big break is enough for me!"

Ali donated the proceeds from her first single to Yasmin's charity. And every time I see Ali Thorn's name on a new album, it thrills me to know that I played a part in getting her there!

punk Funk

Use your fashion design colouring pencils to complete this picture of Sasha and her friends with their new punk look!

Kakuro Conundrum

How fast can you complete this tricky Kakuro puzzle?

		22 \	17 \			11 \	29 \
	6 \ 9			29 \	5 \ 12		
\ 41							
\ 6			4 \ 11				
\ 15					11 \ 8		
	11 \	22 \ 6				29 \	15 \
\ 10			10 \ 29				
\ 29					4 \ 10		
\ 29							
\ 4				\ 6			

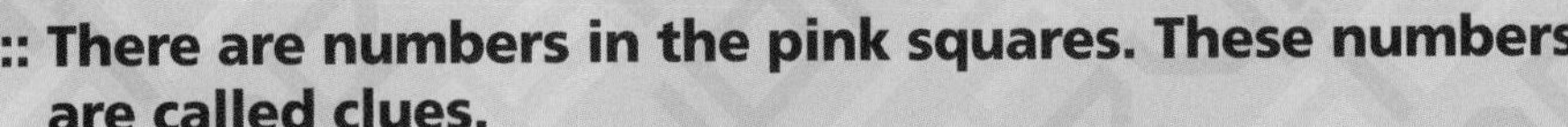

- There are numbers in the pink squares. These numbers are called clues.
- The lines in the puzzle should be read from top to bottom and from right to left
- Each pink square is divided by a diagonal slash. The number in the top right corner is an 'across' clue. The number in the bottom left corner is a 'down' clue.
- You must insert numbers from 1 to 9 into the white squares to add up to the clue.
- You can't repeat any number twice in each sum.

breakfast

Greek yoghurt, honey and summer fruits

The perfect breakfast dish for warm mornings!

1 small pot Greek yoghurt
10 strawberries
Half a melon
2 plums
2 fresh figs
1 peach
Honey

1. Take a large plate and pour the Greek yoghurt into the centre.
2. Cut the plums into quarters and remove the stones. Make sure you ask your 'rents to help you when you're using a knife.
3. Cut the peach in half and remove the stone. Then cut the peach into thick slices.
4. Peel and slice the figs.
5. Remove the skin of the melon and de-seed it. Then cut it into small squares.
6. Cut the strawberries in half.
7. Arrange the fruit around the outside of the plate, making a fan around the yoghurt.
8. Drizzle everything with honey.

Orange Delight

A delicious and refreshing orange drink.

3 fl oz orange juice
4 fl oz water
4 fl oz milk
½ tsp vanilla extract
1 tbsp sugar
Ice cubes

1. Put the milk, water and vanilla extract into a blender.
2. Stir in the orange juice and sugar.
3. Turn on the blender and slowly add the ice cubes, one by one. Keep going until the mixture is as thick as you want it to be.
4. Serve in tall glasses.

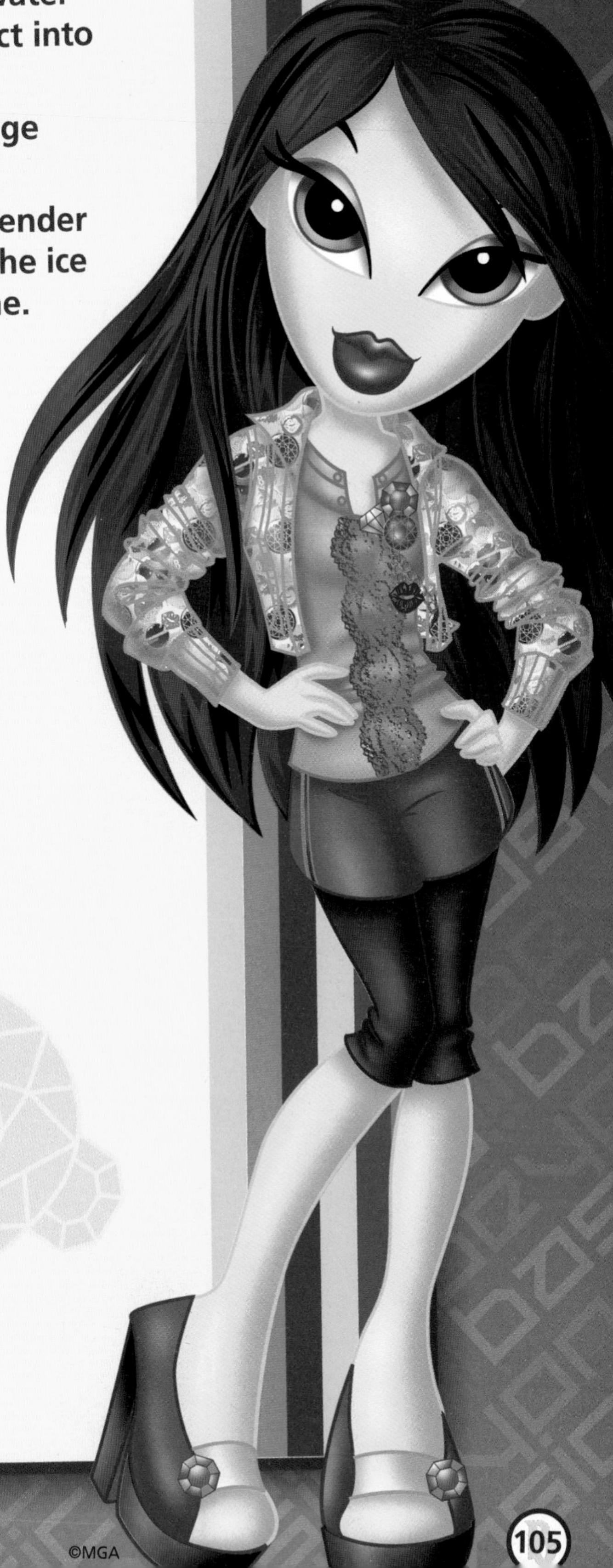

Vegetarian Chilli

A delicious, spicy dish.

1 tbsp oil
2 cloves garlic, crushed
1 onion, chopped
1 tin sweetcorn
1 tin chopped tomatoes
1 tin kidney beans
1 cauliflower, cut into florets
1 large potato, diced
1 green pepper, chopped
2 carrots, chopped
2 celery stalks, chopped
8 oz mushrooms, chopped
2 tbsp tomato puree
1 tbsp cumin
1 tbsp chilli powder
1 tsp paprika
Pinch of cayenne pepper
Pinch of salt
$^1/_2$ pint water

Tip: If you wish, you can add soya mince to the mixture. Experiment with your favourite vegetables to create your perfect chilli.

1. Heat the oil in a large, thick-bottomed saucepan.

2. Add the onion and garlic and fry over a medium heat for five minutes.

3. Add the mushrooms and cook for ten minutes.

4. Add all the other ingredients and bring to the boil.

5. Reduce the heat, cover the pan and simmer for about 30 minutes, until the vegetables are tender.

Important!

Always get your 'rents to help you when you're chopping vegetables or working with a hot oven or stove.

Cheese and Potato Hotpot

A delicious, filling winter meal.

$1\frac{1}{2}$ lb boiled potatoes, sliced

4 oz grated cheddar cheese

2 eggs, beaten

1 tbsp milk

Thyme

Salt

Pepper

Butter

Breadcrumbs

A greased casserole dish with a lid

1. Preheat the oven to 190 C, Gas Mark 4.
2. Cover the base of the dish with potato slices.
3. Pour a quarter of the beaten egg over the potatoes.
4. Sprinkle a little thyme, salt and pepper over the potatoes and egg.
5. Cover with a layer of grated cheese.
6. Repeat steps 2–5 twice, so you end up with three layers.
7. Pour the remaining egg and the milk over the final layer.
8. Add three knobs of butter and sprinkle with breadcrumbs.
9. Put the lid on the dish and bake for 25 minutes.
10. Remove the lid and cook for another five minutes to crisp the top.
11. Serve with your fave vegetables!

make a recipe book

If you love cooking, you'll want to keep all your fave recipes together in one place. The recipe book you start now will stay with you for the rest of your life, and you will just keep adding fabulous and delicious recipes to it.

You will need:

2 pieces of thick cardboard, 15cm wide and 22cm long. (These will be your book covers.)

Glue or double-sided sticky tape

2 pieces of your fave fabric, 14cm wide and 21cm long.

2 larger pieces of the same fabric, 17cm wide by 24cm long.

Thick ribbon to match your fabric

Glitter, craft decorations

A5 paper

Hole punch

1. Stick one of the smaller pieces of fabric to one side of the first cardboard cover. Do the same for the second cardboard cover.

2. Lay one piece of fabric on a table with the good side against the table.

3. Put glue or double-sided sticky tape on the cardboard side of one cover.

4. Lay the cover on top of the fabric, sticky side down.

5. Cut off the corners of the fabric and stick it down around the sides of the cover. You should not be able to see any cardboard now.

6. Repeat steps 2–5 for the second cover.

7. Punch two holes at the side of the covered cardboard.

8. Use your craft materials to create a totally unique cover for your recipe book. You might want to write your name, or the year that you started it.

9. Punch holes at the side of the A5 paper.

10. Place the paper in between the two cardboard covers, and thread the ribbon through the holes to hold the book together. Hold in place with two double bows. You can always untie these to add more paper later – your book will be as thick as you make it!

ANSWERS

PAGE 16
Weird Wordsearch

G	H	O	U	T	E	R	S	U	A	B	P	H	A	N	T	O	M
K	H	B	C	F	R	W	J	I	U	D	E	H	O	G	X	A	A
F	T	O	H	A	E	R	C	S	P	E	C	O	A	U	E	L	E
L	U	C	S	T	U	N	P	W	I	G	T	E	Y	R	L	E	R
A	E	O	R	T	E	E	R	I	E	J	R	Y	S	H	M	G	L
R	H	O	U	W	C	K	U	L	T	N	U	A	H	E	V	L	U
U	S	K	H	T	R	U	C	R	U	D	S	N	A	K	W	E	O
T	O	I	R	N	G	F	O	R	I	D	U	K	S	C	O	B	H
A	P	E	M	U	H	O	N	C	R	A	T	O	I	U	E	L	G
N	E	B	C	A	O	K	O	O	T	U	N	O	L	R	B	H	M
R	N	P	U	T	U	L	P	B	I	P	A	P	T	S	O	U	L
E	W	O	I	V	D	B	E	W	O	T	M	S	H	E	U	C	S
P	I	N	R	J	E	B	N	E	U	O	I	T	I	H	I	S	N
U	N	I	E	T	R	O	D	B	S	M	G	R	E	L	P	I	R
S	M	A	E	R	C	S	B	S	T	A	P	P	A	R	D	O	E
W	R	I	N	C	H	T	P	U	B	D	A	R	R	P	E	N	P
R	U	S	D	N	E	E	I	R	E	T	O	E	N	U	P	T	U
U	E	R	C	S	H	A	D	O	W	S	E	R	U	D	H	A	S

PAGE 39
Crossword

1. B I G T O P
2. P I E S
3. R I N G M A S T E R
4. S I D E S H O W S
5. A C R O B A T S
6. B A R E B A C K
7. N O S E S
8. R O L L U P
9. T R A P E Z E

PAGE 82
Wordsearch

R	J	S	R	S	A	L	I	B	R	H	N	F	D
E	L	T	R	O	U	S	E	R	S	M	S	A	R
P	A	R	X	D	C	F	Q	J	O	I	K	O	H
M	G	O	I	B	U	T	L	L	Y	H	E	C	D
U	W	H	S	U	L	R	B	O	O	E	A	M	X
J	D	S	B	W	I	O	D	A	C	M	Z	S	N
U	L	M	C	D	O	Y	U	L	I	G	K	U	R
B	T	I	D	T	S	K	H	S	L	U	W	B	G
A	R	J	S	J	X	E	O	H	E	A	T	E	Q
S	I	T	Q	S	W	L	G	K	S	D	A	I	W
I	K	C	A	R	E	H	M	Z	U	L	O	M	B
D	S	X	U	G	K	I	D	R	A	X	C	A	E
Q	J	T	W	S	S	E	R	D	T	B	U	J	L
B	D	H	L	R	I	K	T	S	F	U	O	R	T

PAGE 64
Puzzle Page

8	9	7	5	3	2	1	6	4
3	1	6	4	8	7	2	9	5
4	2	5	9	6	1	7	3	8
1	8	4	3	5	9	6	2	7
6	3	2	7	1	8	4	5	9
7	5	9	6	2	4	8	1	3
9	7	1	2	4	5	3	8	6
5	6	8	1	7	3	9	4	2
2	4	3	8	9	6	5	7	1

7	1	5	2	3	8	4	6	9
2	9	3	4	5	6	7	8	1
8	4	6	9	7	1	3	2	5
1	7	4	6	8	2	5	9	3
3	5	2	1	9	7	6	4	8
9	6	8	3	4	5	1	7	2
4	2	9	5	6	3	8	1	7
6	3	7	8	1	9	2	5	4
5	8	1	7	2	4	9	3	6

3	8	7	4	1	9	5	6	2
9	6	1	5	2	3	7	8	4
4	2	5	8	6	7	3	1	9
2	5	3	1	7	8	4	9	6
8	9	4	3	5	6	1	2	7
1	7	6	2	9	4	8	3	5
7	3	8	9	4	2	6	5	1
5	4	9	6	8	1	2	7	3
6	1	2	7	3	5	9	4	8

9	7	1	5	2	4	3	8	6
2	3	5	8	6	1	7	9	4
8	4	6	7	3	9	2	1	5
4	5	8	2	7	6	9	3	1
6	1	3	9	4	8	5	2	7
7	2	9	3	1	5	4	6	8
1	9	2	4	8	7	6	5	3
5	8	4	6	9	3	1	7	2
3	6	7	1	5	2	8	4	9

PAGE 103
Kakuro Conundrum

		22\	17\			11\	29\
	6\9	1	8	29\	5\12	3	9
\41	2	7	9	6	4	5	8
\6	1	5	4\11	3	1	2	5
\15	3	9	1	2	11\8	1	7
	11\	22\6	3	1	2	29\	15\
\10	1	9	10\29	5	9	7	8
\29	5	7	9	8	4\10	9	1
\29	2	5	1	4	3	8	6
\4	3	1		\6	1	5	